CW00918582

GARDENS OF DELIGHT

by

James Kelway

Copyright - introduction © Dave Root
The moral right of Dave Root to be identified as the author of the introduction to this work has been
asserted by him in accordance with the Copyright, Designs and Patents Act 1988.

All rights reserved. No part of this publication may be reproduced, stored in a retrieval system or
transmitted in any form or by any means, electronic, mechanical, photocopying, recording or
otherwise, without the prior permission of both the copyright owner and the publisher of this book.

First published in 1909 by Kelway & Son of Langport; 2nd revised edition published in 1914.
This reprint published in paperback in Great Britain in 2014 by Picts Hill Publishing,
an imprint of Even Handed Licensing Limited

ISBN **978-1-904496-09-0**

Printed in Great Britain by the Somerton Printery

Picts Hill Publishing
Even Handed Licensing Limited
PO Box 93
Langport
TA10 1AP

Kelways Heritage Series No.3

INTRODUCTION

Kelways' *Gardens of Delight* was originally published in 1909 as a supplement to Kelways' *Manual of Horticulture*, which was the firm's annual catalogue. These were wondrous tomes stretching to several hundred pages, containing detailed listings of the nursery's many thousands of plants and products. *Gardens of Delight*, which was extensively revised for this 1914 edition, was used to showcase the pioneering work done by Kelways in improving some of our most popular garden plants, but in particular peonies, delphiniums, pyrethrums, and gladiolus. For these plants Kelway & Son were the envy of the world, and this book demonstrated how these improved forms could be used for maximum effect in the garden.

The Kelways' work did not end at improving garden plants for greater floriferousness, fortitude in the border, scent and richness of colour; they were also pioneers in the new movement that was called the 'artistic border'. Gardening per se had always been the preserve of the wealthy, and those with plenty of space, time and money, and was quite distinct from the cottage gardener who grew subsistence vegetables and fruits cheek by jowl with a few flowers for effect and for attracting bees.

In the spring the grand border would be planted out with bedding plants, calendula, petunia, amaranthus and all kinds of tender perennials which had been expensively propagated and reared in warm glasshouses during the winter. Then in the autumn, the whole lot was ripped out to be replaced by spring flowering bulbs, pansies, wallflowers and sweet williams. The owners of these great and also of the more modest houses rarely worried about what plants were used so long as it was constantly colourful, and they were happy to pay the heating bills and labour costs. There was rarely any harmony in the colours used - it was all about the show.

Eventually some of the more forward thinking designers of the day started to challenge this way of planting, most notably Gertrude Jekyll and William Robinson. Their vision was that of the permanently planted perennial border, which brought a living blank canvas which could be planted artistically, to give colour, form and beauty for the whole of the growing season. It was suggested that for every flower that thrived with heat and constant coaxing there were 50 still lovelier that thrived in ordinary fresh air and that flowered with greater vigour, colour and scent.

These permanently planted borders needed far less maintenance than the old bedded out borders. However this style of planting was certainly no soft option. The ideal depth for a border was suggested to be no less than 12ft. Soil preparation was intense, thorough and unrelenting. The border needed to be dug over to a depth of a minimum of 2.5 feet, with copious amounts of farmyard manure dug in prior to planting. If the soil was anything less than ideal it was often suggested that the whole lot be removed and replaced with a heavenly medium loam blend, so that in a dry summer the plants did not suffer though lack of water.

Thus a unity of purpose was formed between Gertrude Jekyll and firms such as Kelway & Son. She was able to work more successfully with the improved forms of plants produced by Kelways, and her pioneering work on colour schemes promoted the market for this type of artistic border which fuelled the improvement work of the nurserymen. The design emphasis was focused on colour, which came primarily from flowers. There was less interest in foliage, and perennials were never mixed with shrubs, which were firmly confined to the "shrubbery".

An artistic border planted for colour, "should be a thing of beauty for at least 8 months of the year." Gertrude Jekyll believed that once someone had seen a flower border arranged for colour they would never go back to haphazard planting again. "It seems to me that the duty we owe to our gardens," she said in her book *Colour schemes for the flower garden*, "is to so use the plants that they shall form beautiful pictures." A garden may contain the best plants, and the gardener the most able, but if the plants are not placed to good effect the border will not be a success.

Some of the other self-imposed parameters set by the Kelways were that fully 50% of the flowers in the border should be suitable for cutting for the house. "And in every month flowers" was their most confident statement of all. "The best way to get year round beauty is not to make a list of your favourite flowers, but instead to make a list of the months and make sure each month has several plants of interest."

Three basic principles of colour were used in the design of the finest herbaceous borders: contrast, analogy, and graduation. The relationship of one colour to another is the contrast, and is based upon the 3 primary colours of red, blue and yellow. The contrast colour should contain the primary colour that the other lacks. Thus purple delphiniums (blue and red) contrast with yellow, and green astrantia (blue and yellow) contrast with red poppies.

Analogy is a more difficult principle which deals with colours that are related, and which when placed together mutually improve and strengthen each other.

Graduation is the sometimes imperceptible blending and drifting of one colour into another. It could mean a white geranium with a pink tinge blending into a deeper coloured phlox, with edges of precisely the same hue as the former. The size of each mass of colour should be large enough to have a certain dignity, but never so large as to be wearisome.

When a long border is planted in a colour drift, then plants of the same colour but flowering at different times should be planted close to each other, ie red gladioli and red wallflowers, so that the colour theme is maintained even though individual plants will peak at different times.

There can also be a progression of colour along the length of a border, and some were very long indeed - 100 yards was not considered that impressive! This allowed a really beautiful sweep of colour from one end to the other. A border might begin with strong blues, grouped with white and pale yellow, passing on to pink and then rose, crimson and finally the strongest scarlet, leading to orange and bright yellow at the farthest end.

It seems obvious that Miss Jekyll would have worked with James Kelway to develop the artistic borders, for she publicly saluted the firm for its efforts in plant improvement.

Kelways devised 20 different artistic borders for general year round interest; borders which peaked in one of the four seasons; borders for north and south facing aspects, and borders dominant in a single colour. All were provided with planting plans, with the plants carefully numbered.

There were also 20 slightly cheaper border selections, for cut flowers in spring, summer or autumn, ideal for a border in a garden of a house where the owner only visited for a few weeks a year. Borders composed of plants suitable for different soils, taller or shorter plant selections, sunny aspects and colder situations could also be provided.

The nursery would also supply all of the extras that might be needed, including garden seats, trellis, fertiliser, rock, and beautifully cast plant labels. They had it all covered. They were perhaps the pioneers of the design based shops such as Laura Ashley, yet instead of a bespoke designed room using matching components, the house owner could choose the whole herbaceous border and its accessories from Kelways, knowing that collectively it would be sublime, elegant and beautiful, yet available 'off the peg'.

Herbaceous borders composed of hardy perennials arranged according to colour and season of blooming did more to increase the enjoyment of gardening and decrease the cost than any horticultural development of the era. To some extent they were taking over the planning role that used to be the preserve of the Head Gardeners. Little did Kelways know just how important this would continue to be, because World War One was gathering momentum as the very ink was drying on this 1914 book. The grand houses lost much of their labour force to the war effort, and many of the gardeners never returned. The nursery in Somerset was no different, and many staff were lost during the war. Thus this book celebrates the very zenith of the grand herbaceous border at a moment when the world was about to change forever.

Dave Root
April 2014

GARDENS

of

DELIGHT

by

JAMES KELWAY

SUPPLEMENT

to the

MANUAL

of

HORTICULTURE

KELWAY & SON   LANGPORT

A NOTE *by* MISS JEKYLL

written expressly for
KELWAY'S MANUAL

AS the years go by the love of gardening always grows. Latterly, the growth has been in a much-needed direction, namely, that of a wiser discrimination in the use of material. With the better knowledge of plants, owners of gardens are concerning themselves with learning which are the very best varieties, and further, with their better use by means of good arrangement and careful grouping for colour effect.

The notable work of the owners of the great gardens at Langport has been perceptibly stimulated by the thoughtful writing and personal sympathy of the recent leaders in horticulture; the result of this wholesome stimulus, acting on long-sustained effort and unwearied patience, is now seen in the wealth of splendid flowers in all the best classes of hardy plants for which these renowned gardens are justly famous.

Gertrude Jekyll

KELWAY GARDENS & KELWAY HERBACEOUS BORDERS

The GARDEN BEAUTIFUL *and* ECONOMICAL

THE formation of actual scenes of beauty with living subjects abounding in interest individually would seem to be a pleasant and worthy amusement and one as full of dignity as the portrayal of such scenes on paper or canvas.

¶ Wordsworth, in a beautiful passage, pointed out this truth and at the same time indicated a path along which many have travelled before, as well as, and particularly, since his time. "Laying out grounds," he wrote, "may be considered as a liberal art, in some sort like poetry and painting; and its object, like that of all the liberal arts, is, or ought to be, to move the affections under the control of good sense."

COLOUR SCHEMES *in the* GARDEN

BY JAMES KELWAY

To the Editor of *Gardening Illustrated*.

SIR,—I have read ————'s remarks in *Gardening Illustrated*, April 8th, and agree entirely with the premises but not altogether with the inferences.

The old system of propagating in expensive glasshouses great quantities of tender plants during the spring, in order that they might be "bedded out" in exceedingly stiff and glaring masses, to bloom for a short time during the summer, *was* "tyranny." One was a victim of the result, unsatisfactory from an artistic point of view, of the wearisome repetition of the same patterned arrangement year by year, and of the great expenditure of money and waste of energy and material inseparable from the methods. There was "tyranny" in the constant use of this unsatisfactory system by victims who might abhor what they got, but who continued in the embraces of the tyrant because they were ignorant of the means of release. There was no reason why their resident horticultural mentor should release them. Quite the contrary. And in all probability he was equally ignorant of any alternative.

The honoured founder of this journal, and Miss Jekyll, arose to preach the requisite crusade against such limited ideals. Years passed before any but private efforts were made to make the war really effective. An early and willing convert, I experimented with perennial border plants, planned arrangements and colour schemes of various kinds, and as a result, through my firm, offered to the public "borders" arranged ready for planting. Apparently they are appreciated. We have planned borders of all kinds, but we find that clients generally prefer to touch the whole gamut of colour, and that they usually order that particular kind of border. But there is no "tyranny" here. Many have their borders arranged in the style that ———— himself prefers. Some have a liking for certain colours, and wish others omitted; many prefer bold contrasts in colour and form, while others like harmonies; to many, again, and for certain positions, a broad treatment is attractive. Proprietors of gardens who are not horticultural experts need no longer be the slaves of their employees in the matter of their flower garden, and it has become a pleasant duty for the gardener to adapt himself, under the alternative scheme, to the taste of his employer, as seems right.

THE IDEA OF PERMANENT BORDERS OF PERENNIALS arranged for colour effect and for succession through the year has captured the public mind, but the ways in which the principles applied need by no means be stereotyped. One graduated scheme of colouring ranging from one end to the other of the colour gamut may be very charming, but it need by no means be adhered to or made a fetish. In fact it is only suitable for rather large borders. There is ample "liberty"; freedom for schemes and plann-

IN MY GARDEN THIS MORNING

JANUARY 10. While the country gardener has to contend with moles and rabbits, the town gardener has often to wage war against the unromantic cat.

Where cats are troublesome the garden should be surrounded with wire netting, the top left to hang loosely. Chloride of lime or wet tar placed on the tops of walls will help to keep them away.

Mice will soon be on the look-out for the white shoots of the crocuses. Later on sparrows may, if unchecked, work havoc among the flowers.

Mouse-traps must therefore be set at once.

Black cotton stretched above the crocuses keeps most birds at bay.

KELWAY'S "ARTISTIC" BORDERS

No. 1 "A" Kelway "Artistic" permanent general border. £5 0s. 0d. per 100 strong plants, or 10 square yards for 25/-; 100 square yards 250/-, arranged for continuous bloom and colour effect.

"IF this be so when we are merely putting together words or colours, how much more ought the feeling to prevail when we are in the midst of realities of things ; of the beauty and harmony, of the joy and happiness of living creatures ; of men and children, of birds and beasts, of hills and streams, and trees and flowers, with the changes of night and day, evening and morning, summer and winter, and all their unwearied actions and energies?"

¶ It is recognised that gardening is the most healthful of hobbies, and that gardeners are longer lived than men of any class. And so this side of gardening has become in this country in recent years a popular and fashionable recreation amongst people of leisure and taste, who are bringing their own refinement and knowledge to bear ; and a great improvement is seen in the arrangement of gardens.

¶ The ideal of "IN EVERY MONTH FLOWERS"—flowers in the spring, flowers in the summer, flowers in the autumn, even in winter flowers or painted foliage—is each year coming nearer realisation. Tennyson hinted at an ideal garden when he sang ".... the daughters of the year one after one through that still garden passed, and each in passing touched with some new grace."

ings of all kinds during the first arrangement, and the opportunity for improvement or alterations, "to taste" as the cookery books have it, in succeeding seasons. Amateur gardeners, fascinated, spend the fine days of late autumn and early spring in alterations for which they made notes during flower-time, and on summer evenings they hover trowel in hand, inventing and trying new effects.

From his letter I should think ―――― may be one of those who hover. But who could spend time in the same way over "carpet bedding" unless he were quite devoid of poetry or were paid to do it ? And, although a paper planting-plan of a colour border looks to some extent formal, the plants in the border have not this effect in the slightest when they flower. The plants of one colour are not all abloom together, of one height and aspect—flat, uniform masses of yellow Calceolaria, or scarlet Pelargonium, or magenta Petunia. Far from it. They are a continual surprise and delight as they open. Every week, or at any rate, every fortnight, the border entirely varies. And that which ―――― likes, the opportunity for the idolisation of his particular favourites, can be carried into effect with the utmost facility by planting strong groups of them,

so that at certain seasons they may dominate the scheme.

The new scheme is not wrong because it is a "Scheme"—the outcome of thought based on knowledge. The most beautiful picture is the work of the best thinker as well as of the cleverest painter ; and it is not helpful to gibe at borders being "sold at so much a yard," so long as they are not planned in the spirit of a yard measure. Even a Velasquez is sold on some basis, and Rubens had, possibly with reluctance, to fit his figures to the area of his canvas, like any other mortal. The happy fact is, that the border can be procured, and it is a matter for congratulation that it is possible for those who themselves have not the necessary time or knowledge, to obtain the realisation of their artistic desires in this easy manner, and that those who love certain kinds of plants above other kinds are not only allowed by tyrant fashion to grow them, but are shown how to arrange them as and where they appear to advantage with other flowers of harmonious or contrasting beauty, instead of being obliged to see them huddled together in atrocious concatenations of colour, or spotted about at regular yard-measure intervals. Many a border one sees is for all the world like the dot and comma masterpiece of a dado-stencilling house-painter.

If ―――― complains of exaggeration, I agree—when I see it. But until I observe someone endeavouring to fill, not only his herbaceous borders, but every unsuitable bed and corner of his place, with some one patented plan, I shall vote in the other lobby. If one's eye tells one that a pink flower does not go well near a scarlet, and if other people are saved from unwittingly planting the two quarrelsome tints together because one has pointed the fact out, one has done a service, and the public need not be accused of slavishly following fresh fashions if they benefit by the information. But I agree

IN MY GARDEN THIS MORNING

JANUARY 20. The fair-weather gardener is never successful. A gardener must be prepared to face wind and rain should occasion arise. Though little work can be done out-of-doors this month, the following hints may be useful.

Soot should now be sprinkled over the borders. Plants put in last autumn must be trodden round after severe weather, as the frost tends to raise them.

Old rubbish heaps can be gone over and sifted. Decayed vegetation is a good fertiliser.

Dead wood must be cut out of trees and burnt. Wood-ash is a valuable plant-food, as it contains potash, soda, phosphoric acid, and magnesia.

KELWAY'S "ARTISTIC" BORDERS

No. 1 "B" at 60/- per 100 ; 10 square yards 15/- ; 100 square yards 150/-.

THE late Dean Hole truthfully wrote in "Our Gardens": "There has been no introduction which has had such happy and universal influence in extending and increasing the enjoyment of a garden as the HERBACEOUS BORDER." One of the first remarks of one's hostess in the country now-a-days is, "would you care to see my new Herbaceous Border?"—in many cases "my new **Kelway** Border."

¶ Those who are aware that the greatest art is that which has succeeded in concealing the skill from which it springs—*ars celare artem*—and who want surpassingly beautiful gardens, should not complete their gardening schemes without first considering the Kelway plans for Herbaceous Borders arranged by expert knowledge with a view to colour effect and continuous bloom. Our "Artistic" system is being extended to other parts of the garden, and "Kelway Gardens" are becoming known everywhere as true "GARDENS OF DELIGHT." The disposition of heights and colours in these pre-arranged Borders is correct, but does not err on the side of formality. For the "stars of earth," flowers should be disposed with no niggard hand, but as far as possible like the stars of heaven, in spreading groups and constellations, and if particulars of soil and aspect are sent us, colour schemes are evolved which are a delight for many months of many succeeding years—a joy increasing as the plants grow in loveliness with each season. Applied to the flower garden as a whole the scheme supplies not only a GARDEN BEAUTIFUL but a GARDEN ECONOMICAL, as the most gorgeous and pleasing effects from spring to late autumn are obtained without the use of glass and with very little trouble, and flat carpet bedding is reduced to its proper proportions. In days gone by there was in many gardens a painfully blinding blaze as of an ephemeral fiery torch, and then the succeeding blackness and gloom lasting until nine or ten months had rolled by. Our Artistic Herbaceous borders, on the other hand, composed chiefly of hardy perennial plants, arranged according to their season of blooming, become a PERENNIAL PLEASURE, and have done more to increase the enjoyment of gardening, and decrease the cost than any horticultural development of recent years.

that if fashion decreed that all borders must now "pass from red to blue and from blue to yellow by arbitrary gradations," it would be a pity. But there are so many beautiful arrangements possible; their number is without end, and they are infinitely interesting. It is open for the amateur himself to discover many of them.

———— says it is laid down that a GROUP OF ONE KIND OF FLOWER MAY NOT BE REPEATED.—I do not know where this is taught. It must be by some false prophet, who has not the root of the matter in him. In a large border favourite flowers may recur as often as desired and space will allow, only let them not come, like telegraph poles or urban lamp-posts, at measured intervals, nor exhibit their beauty in close proximity with flowers whose colour tones lessen their loveliness. ———— thinks all this is "gardening from a distance." The effect of such a border is certainly exceedingly attractive from a distance, long or short, but this is an additional merit; there is no subordination of individuality to the general effect; the genesis of the idea was rather otherwise. Breadth of treatment cannot affect the individuality of a plant or group; plants are not like brush marks on a canvas, unmeaning on close inspection. A great painter said of his pictures that they were "not meant to be smelt," but this does not apply to flower-borders. I am entirely in accord with ———— when he speaks of the beauty of borders with one or two families of flowers in their season; as he says: "Nature gives us Primrose-time and Bluebell time, and the effect is perfect." I have planned Michaelmas Daisy borders and Pæony borders, and other special borders, with the help of a few suitable bulbous or other flowers. Blue borders, for example, are a delight. But the general public likes general borders,

and, after all, the public is the master or tyrant, and no one else—as is proper. Even the public, however, may be **guided,** and, I find, is grateful for such little assistance as it may be in the power of those with more experience to give.

————'s criticism makes for good if it is understood as a criticism of the way in which the best of ideals may be spoiled at the hands of those who have not properly grasped the essentials. But is it worth while saying anything which may be mistaken as condemnation of those essentials rightly handled? JAMES KELWAY.

Wearne Wyche, Langport.

BORDERS *of* HARDY FLOWERS

By WILLIAM ROBINSON

As during all time a simple border has been the first expression of flower gardening, and as there is no arrangement of flowers more graceful, varied, or capable of giving more

IN MY GARDEN THIS MORNING

JANUARY 30. Several days last week it was pleasant to wander through the garden and find that the frost had departed.

Life in the world seemed suddenly to awake. In the meadows young lambs were bleating. Overhead skylarks carolled joyously. The sun was warm, the breeze gentle. Snowdrops were raising their heads again. One could almost see the winter aconites opening their golden buds.

Now, although the frost has returned again, we have heard spring calling from afar. Let those who only "enjoy" their gardens during the summer go forth on a January morning, so full of promise, so throbbing with joy.

KELWAY'S "ARTISTIC" BORDERS

No. 2 "A" Spring Flowering Border. In flower from February to the end of May, arranged on Kelway "Artistic" plan of continuous bloom and colour effect. Prices same as No. 1 "A."

A COMBINATION of the beautiful and practical has driven away the age of the Brussels carpet from our gardens as woolwork and stuffed birds have been ousted from our drawing-rooms. There is no bare ground in a garden arranged on this plan : every portion of earth is made to yield its quota of beauty—beauty without a break from the birth of the year, "when spring unlocks the flowers to paint the laughing soil," until the ground is frost-bound ; and even then there are floral gems—the "gems with which fair Nature decks herself"—gleaming here and there amid the snow. So that the enjoyment of a garden is extended and at the same time increased.

¶ This is the basis of the garden of to-day—the KELWAY GARDEN. All its contents, at desire, may be the products of our open fields of hardy plants here at Langport, natives or exotics which have proved themselves to be acclimatised in every part of Great Britain, Ireland and those parts of Europe and America and the Colonies which lie within the temperate zone. Strong, healthy, and freshly dug, they start, without check or hindrance, on their mission of providing enjoyment. **Old English Flowers for New English Gardens,** with the addition of all the last improvements in form and colour.

delight, and none so easily adapted to almost every kind of garden, some idea of the various kinds of borders of hardy flowers mainly deserves our first consideration.

COST AND ENDURANCE.—The difference in cost of growing hardy flowers or tender should be thought of. The sacrifice of flower gardens to plants that perish every year has often left them poor of all the nobler plants. We must take into account the hot-houses, the propagation of plants by thousands at certain seasons, the planting out at the busiest and fairest time of the year—in June—the digging up and storing in autumn, the care in winter. There are a number of things which, given thorough preparation at first, it would be wise to leave alone for some years at a time—as, for example, groups or beds of the various Tritomas, Irises, Lilies, Pæonies, the free-flowering Yuccas, Narcissi—these and many more either grouped with others or in families. When all these exhaust the ground or become too crowded, by all means move them and replant, but this is a very different thing from moving all the plants in the flower garden twice a year. It would be better every way if, so far as the flower garden is concerned, gardeners were to see what could

be done unaided by the hot-house ; but meanwhile, the wise man will reduce the expense of glass, labour, fire, repairs, paint, pipes, and boilers to something like reasonable proportions. In presence of the wealth of our hardy garden flora, *the promise of which is now such as men never expected a few years ago,* **no one need doubt of making a fair flower garden from hardy plants alone.** *The true way to make gardens yield a return of beauty for the labour and skill given them is the permanent one. Choose some beautiful class of plants and select a place that will suit them,* even as to their effect in the garden landscape. *Let the beds be planted as permanently and as well as possible, so that there will remain little to do for years.* All plants may not lend themselves to this permanent plan, but such as do not may be grown apart—for instance, the Poppy, Anemones, Turban and Persian Ranunculi, Carnations, Stocks, Asters, and the finer annuals. But a great many delightful plants can be planted permanently and be either allowed to arrange themselves to group with others, or to grow among peat-loving shrubs, which, in many places, are jammed into pudding-shaped masses void of form or grace, or light and shade . . . . There are many groups to be made by the aid of the finer perennials themselves, such as the Delphiniums and Phloxes, by choosing things that would go well together. . . . .

No plan which involves expensive yearly efforts *on the same piece of ground* can ever be satisfactory. All garden plants require attention, but not annual attention. The true way is quite different—the devotion of the skill and effort to fresh beds and effects each year. It does not exclude summer "bedding," but includes lovely and varied aspects of vegetation far beyond that attainable in summer "bedding," and

IN MY GARDEN THIS MORNING

FEBRUARY 9. I am writing to-day of an Isle of Wight garden. In coming to "The Island" I have suddenly jumped into spring. February is gone ; it is the middle of March !

Crocuses are full in bloom. Soon the primroses will be at their best. Nothing astonishes one more than the way the laurestinus flowers in warm localties. Here it is one sheet of rosy-white bloom. In many cold places the buds will hardly open.

Those two lovely low-growing plants, the white and purple rock-cress, are a blaze of colour.

It is a veritable peep into the future for a garden-lover.

KELWAY'S "ARTISTIC" BORDERS

No. 2 "B" Spring Flowering Border. In flower from February to the end of May, arranged on the Kelway "Artistic" plan of continuous bloom and colour effect. Prices same as No. 1 "B."

THE enormous value this system has in providing cut flowers for the house must not be forgotten. Fifty per cent. of these hardy flowers can be brought as cut flowers into the room of the house, and nearly as large a proportion are sweet scented ; the majority of them are really as entrancing as greenhouse exotics.

❧

¶ These beautiful schemes of colour are eminently successful only when composed by someone who possesses practical knowledge of plants as well as artistic sense ; a minimum of the latter may suffice, but experience with the flowers to be used is essential, and this is where our services, if we may say so, prove especially valuable. It has been, in fact, only after many experiments and continual elaboration of improvement that we have arrived at colour schemes and borders which have given the result an artistic imagination desired to produce for different seasons and situations. But the resulting feasts of ever-changing colour, unlike the old bedding system, show no *evidence* of painful labour.

❧

¶ To the artistic, colour-loving mind, Hardy Plants form a never-ending pleasure. "Should it not be remembered that in setting a garden we are painting a picture—a picture of hundreds of feet or yards, instead of so many inches, painted with living flowers, and seen by open daylight—so that to paint it rightly is a debt we owe to the beauty of the flowers and to the light of the sun, that the colours should be placed with careful forethought and deliberation, as a painter employs them on his picture, and not dropped down in lifeless dabs ? "

---

attempts to make the garden artistically beautiful. It also helps to make the skill of the gardener effective for lasting good, and prevents its being thrown away in annual fireworks. There can be no gardening without care : but is there not a vast difference between some of these beds and borders and those with flowers which disappear with the frosts of October, and leave us nothing but bare earth ? . . . . Those who notice the ground round country seats find now and then a house without any flower garden, and with the turf running hard into the walls—the site of a flower garden without flowers This unhappy omission we may suppose to result from the ugliness in summer and the nakedness in winter of the common way of planting a flower garden.

But it is a mistake to suppose that the only alternative to such nakedness are coarse perennials and annuals that flower a short time and are weedy the rest of their days, or the ordinary summer planting. Many delightful things may be grown near a house ; fragrant plants, too, plants not only beautiful in summer but in colour even in winter. The ceaseless digging about of the beds also may prejudice people against flowers in the garden, as the bedding plants set out in June were taken away in autumn, and replaced by spring-flowering things. These had a short period of bloom in spring, and were, in their turn, pulled up, leaving bare beds until the summer flowers were planted, sometimes very late ; so that in June, when we ought to have flowers, or at least pleasant colour wholly over the ground, there was nothing but grave-like earth. But the spring flowers round a country house should be grown in a different way. They may be naturalised in multitudes, grown in borders, in special little gardens for bulbs, and in various other ways, without in the least disturbing the beds near the house, which should for

the most part be planted permanently, so that the greatest amount of beauty may be had throughout the fine months without disfiguring the beds during those months. *But the permanent flowers should be hardy, and of the highest order of beauty,* and such as require more than a few weeks or months for development ; though here and there blanks might be filled with good, tender plants, like Heliotrope. . . . .

In growing fine things—Lilies or Cardinal Flowers, or tall Evening Primroses, Pæonies, Delphiniums, Michaelmas Daisies, Day Lilies, Doronicums, etc., etc., among open bushes we may form a delightful garden ; we secure sufficient space for the bushes to show their forms and we get light and shade among them. In such plantations one might have in the back parts " secret " colonies of lovely things which it might not be well to show in the front of the border, or which required shade and shelter that the front did not afford.

BORDERS OR GRASS WALKS IN SHADE OR SUN.—It is not only in the flower garden where we may have much beauty of flower, but away from it there are many places better fitted for growing the more beautiful things

KELWAY'S "ARTISTIC" BORDERS

No. 3. Summer Flowering Border. In flower from May to August, arranged on the Kelway "Artistic" plan of continuous bloom and colour effect. For prices see No. 1 "A" or No. 1 "B."

IN MY GARDEN THIS MORNING

FEBRUARY 19. The suburban gardener must soon set to work if he wants gay borders this year.

Vacant beds should be well dug in dry weather. Hardy annuals (sweet peas, poppies, nasturtiums, etc.), can be sown in March or April. These flowers, if carefully attended to and not grown too thickly, will make a brave show later on.

Then there are the hardy herbaceous plants. They should be planted next month. Phloxes, Michaelmas daisies, campanulas, perennial sunflowers, and many other beautiful subjects, thrive in town gardens. A garden filled with the above flowers is much more interesting than if given up by geraniums, calceolarias, etc. No greenhouse or mysterious "cold pit" will be needed.

HARDY perennial plants are charming in their naturalness and permanence, and it is within the power of every person of taste and information to make a perfect picture of his garden by grouping them artistically, "painting with colours never seen upon a palette." Where we have planned a successful arrangement of it, it may be truly said :—

> " Each beauteous flower,
> Iris, all hues, roses and jessamine,
> Reared high their flourished heads between,
> And wrought mosaic."

In a word, a Kelway Garden exhibits NATURE AT ITS BEST.

¶ The taste for hardy perennial flowers has increased in a very marked degree of late, and we are so interested in assisting by any small means in our power the culture of kinds that can be grown **in the open garden at all seasons without undue expense** that we have systematically added to our collections from home and world-wide sources species which will grow and thrive in this country, until our stock of this class, swollen by the multitude of improved forms which we ourselves have been engaged in raising for over half-a-century, has become the largest in the kingdom, and probably in the world. Our country-grown plants are so large and healthy that every post brings us letters with expressions of grateful appreciation.

¶ We repeat that the initial cost of perennial plants which can be grown in the open air at all seasons is almost the only one attaching to them, which cannot be said of the cultivation of tender plants, annuals or biennials. Hardy Perennial Gardening is equally open to the million and the millionaire, and it affords as much enjoyment to the former as to the latter ; whereas people with moderate incomes contemplate with timidity the cost of the buildings and fuel necessary for the hothouses and greenhouses involved in the cultivation of tender bedding plants. As the author of " Elizabeth and her German Garden " remarks : " No doubt there are many lovely flowers to be had by heat and constant coaxing, but then for each of these there are fifty others still lovelier that will gratefully grow in God's wholesome air and are blessed in return with a far greater intensity of scent and colour."

J. K.

---

which do not require continual attention. . . . . Light and shade and the charm of colour are impossible with heavy dark evergreens, often cut back, but once one is free of their slavery what delightful places there are for growing all hardy flowers in the broad masses, from the handsome Oriental Hellebores of the early spring to the delicate lavenders of the Starworts in October. Not only hardy herbaceous flowers, but graceful climbers like the wild Clematis, and lovely corners of light and shade may be made instead of the walls of sombre evergreens. If we want the ground green with dwarf plants, we have no end of delightful plants at hand in the Ivies, and evergreens like Cotoneaster. There is no need for the labour and ugliness of clipping. I have seen places with acres of detestable clipped Laurels, weary and so ugly ! With all these grubbed and burnt, what places, too, for such beautiful things as the giant Fennels with their more than Fern-like grace, and all our strong, hardy Ferns which want no rocks, with Solomon's Seal & Foxgloves among them. Such walks may pass from open spaces into half-shady ones or through groves of old Fir or other trees, and so give us picturesque variety apart from their planting with flowers.

IN MY GARDEN
THIS MORNING

MARCH 1. Although it is the first of March I am not going to prophesy about the lion and the lamb—they have behaved too erratically in the past !

March may be expected to bring boisterous and drying winds, and a large increase in the amount of sunshine. Towards the end of the month even the most slothful gardener must bestir himself. There will be a hundred things to do.

The garden still looks desolate. Yet several of nature's humbler flowers are in bloom. It will not be long before

> " . . . . the sappy field and wood
> Grow green beneath the showery gray,
> And rugged barks begin to bud . . . ."

FLOWER BORDERS AGAINST WALLS AND HOUSES.—In many situations near houses, and especially old houses, there are delightful opportunities for a very beautiful kind of flower border. The stone forms fine background, and there are no thieving tree roots. Here we have conditions exactly opposite to those in the shrubbery ; here we can have the best soil, and keep it for our favourites ; we can have Delphiniums, Lilies, Pæonies, Irises, and all choice plants well grown. Walls may be adorned with climbers of graceful growth, climbing Rose, Wisteria, Vine, or Clematis, which will help out our beautiful mixed border. These must to some extent be trained, although they may be allowed a certain degree of abandoned grace even on a wall. The variety of good hardy plants is so great that we can make it almost ever green by using evergreen rock plants. Where walls are broken with pillars, a still better effect may be obtained by training Vines and Wisteria along the top and over the pillars or the buttresses.

GENERAL BORDERS may be made in various ways ; but it may be well to bear in mind the following points :— *Select only good plants* ; throw away weedy kinds ; *there is no scarcity of the best—see good collections.* Put, at first, rare kinds in lines across 4 feet nursery beds, so that a stock of plants may be at hand. Make the choicest borders where they cannot be robbed by the roots of trees ; *see that the ground is good and rich, and that it is at least 2½ feet deep, so deep that, in a dry season, the roots can seek their supplies far below the surface. In planting, plant in naturally disposed groups,* never repeating the same plant along the border at intervals, as is so often done with favourites. Do not graduate the plants in height from the front to the back, as is generally done, but sometimes let a

KELWAY'S "ARTISTIC" BORDERS

No. 4. Autumn Flowering Border. In flower from August to late in November, arranged on the Kelway " Artistic " plan of continuous bloom and colour effect. For prices see No. 1 "A" or No. 1 "B."

The PREPARATION *of the* BORDERS *and their* PLANTING

A THING that is worth doing at all is worth doing well, and "Spade-work," recommended by Statesmen, is nowhere so greatly in place as in the garden. Where we contemplate making a permanent border, which we wish to be a "thing of beauty and a joy for ever," spade-work is essential.

¶ The earlier the preparation is put in hand the better; if possible it should be carried out early in the autumn for autumn planting, or in winter for planting in spring.

¶ The digging, or trenching—which is better—should be done to the depth of 2ft. to 2½ft., so that there may be if possible 2ft. of good prepared soil after it has settled. This will frequently do away with the necessity for the continuous watering which one sees in some gardens. When the borders are being dug, all roots of neighbouring shrubs or trees, and all weeds, should be removed from within their limits. When the trenching is being done is the time to improve the soil, by the addition of sandy loam if it be too heavy, or of clayey loam if it be too light; for the working in of rotten leaves or manure. Any **well-decayed** manure is good, but the best is cow-dung, and in using this it must be remembered that it is not for one season it will be required but for many. Do not go in for over-draining; attention to drainage is all right in exceptional soils and for very large borders, but it is not usually necessary; a garden is as a rule well enough drained, and it is good to have some moisture in the soil in the summer.

¶ After the trenching or digging, the soil should be allowed some days, certainly not less than three, to settle.

---

bold plant come to the edge; and, on the other hand, let a little carpet or dwarf plant pass in here and there to the back so as to give a varied instead of a monotonous surface. *Have no patience with bare ground and cover the border with dwarf plants;* do not put them along the front of the border only. Let Hepaticas, and double and other Primroses, and Saxifrages, and Golden Moneywort and Stonecrops, and Forget-me-nots, and dwarf Phloxes, and many similar plants cover the ground among the tall plants betimes—at the back as well as the front. A white Lily will be all the better for having a colony of creeping Forget-me-nots over it in the winter, and the variety that may be thus obtained is infinite. *Thoroughly prepared at first, the border might remain for years without any digging in the usual sense.* When a plant is old and rather too thick, never hesitate to replant it on a wet day in the middle of August any more than in the middle of winter. Take it up and put a fresh bold group in fresh ground; the young plants will have plenty of roots by the winter, and in the following spring will flower much stronger than if they had been transplanted in spring or in winter. WILLIAM ROBINSON.

The above extract, entitled "Borders of Hardy Flowers," is printed by permission of Mr. William Robinson, founder, and for many years editor of *The Garden*, editor of *Gardening Illustrated*, etc., and author of amongst others, that beautiful and invaluable work, *The English Flower Garden.*

Ø

KELWAY'S "ARTISTIC" BORDERS

No. 5. Kelway Blue Border, or a Border of *any* colour or scheme of colour required, either harmonies or contrasts; or a border excluding any colour not liked. Prices as for No. 1 "A" or No. 1 "B."

HARDY BORDERS

By the Late FRANK MILES

If we are to have mixed borders of herbaceous plants one thing is quite certain—we can never go back to the borders of our ancestors, in which every plant had a bare space of ground round it. In the spot where once a plant had bloomed, there was an end for the year of any flowers. *Now a yard of ground should have bloom on it at least eight months in the year,* and this applies to every yard of ground in a really good mixed border. I am certain that once a border is well made, it need not be dug up at all. But the question is—what is a well-made border? I think a border is not well made, or suitable for growing the most beautiful plants to perfection, unless it is as well made as a vine border in a vinery. Why we should not take as much trouble with the garden border as the border of a conservatory I cannot imagine, seeing that Lilies will grow 11 feet high in the open air, not less than 10½ inches across the flower, and Irises little less than that. The more I garden

IN MY GARDEN THIS MORNING

MARCH 12. Sweet-scented flowers appeal to most of us more than those which depend on their beauty only. Summer is the perfect time of sweet scents, but the perfumes of spring are nearly as delicious.

Every garden should hold fragrant flowers. For spring there are hyacinths, primroses, wall-flowers, violets, narcissi, cowslips.

Summer gives us the sweetbriar, sweet rockets, mignonette, the tobacco plant, roses, pinks, carnations, sweet peas, stocks, lavender. An enchanting nosegay!

The night-scented stock is indispensable; a few patches will perfume a large garden after sunset all the summer. It is easy to grow, and may be sown next month.

THE plants in our Artistic Selections on pages 178 and 179 are arranged in order of planting, and it will be found convenient if they be laid out on the ground or turf in front of the border, enough for one day's planting, in the order given in the plans which can be supplied with the plants. In large borders or beds it may be found useful if the yards be pegged off and if lines be stretched at right angles, the pegs and lines being moved as the planting continues. This is merely to show what part of the border the planter has reached, but *by no means in order that the plants may be set out in straight lines.*

¶ As the plants are planted let the soil be pressed in quite firmly around each with boot or hand; the collar of each should be an inch or so below the surface of the soil. Water every plant, especially in dry weather and in late spring; and in the latter case water night and morning for a few days. Save the soft rainwater from the house for this purpose; or river water is preferable to hard water. Finely sifted coal-ash dust should be strewn over and around plants that slugs are fond of, such as Pyrethrums and Delphiniums. Lime when fresh is all right for this purpose, but it cakes with watering, and the slugs can then crawl over it without being harmed. The borders must, of course, be kept free from weeds in the early stages; later on there will be far less "weeding" required—when the borders get covered with plants as it is our intention they should do—than with the ordinary flower bed.

¶ If there are any failures in an autumn-planted border the gaps can be made good in the spring, and likewise in an early spring-planted border. Indeed it is astonishing how well plants take hold and thrive even "out-of-season" if suitable weather be chosen and the plants are strong and carefully moved; under such circumstances transplanting can be carried out throughout the summer. But, if it is preferred, seed of a quick-growing annual may be sown; in the latter case a little judgment and knowledge can be brought to bear in choosing an annual that will "agree" with its neighbours.

¶ There is none of the periodical digging over with these borders, but re-arrangement will often be carried out by those who take an interest in them, and when some plants spread too quickly they can be taken up and divided and portions planted back; all this, with the use of a **Dutch** hoe between the plants, will keep the soil healthy.

---

the deeper I get my drainage, and the fuller of sand and fibre my soil. I consider, first, that a border must have a bed of broken bricks or other drainage, with ashes over that, to prevent the drainage from filling up; secondly, that the bed of drainage must have 2 feet of light soil over it; thirdly, that that soil must have equal parts of sand, soil, and vegetable matter. A soil of three constituents and depth is never wet in winter and never dry in summer. During the dry weather I found soil like this, in which quantities of Auratum Lilies were growing, to be quite moist an inch below the surface, and I know in winter it always appears dry compared with the natural garden soil.

But, for all practical intents and purposes, every 6 inches of ground could contain its plant, so that no 6 inches of bare ground need obtrude on the eye. Almost any kind of bare rock has a certain beauty, but *I cannot say bare ground is ever beautiful.* Well, supposing the back of the border filled with Delphiniums, Phloxes, and Roses, pegged down, and other summer and autumn blooming plants, and supposing the border to be made as I have described it, I should carpet the ground at the back with spring-blooming flowers, so that when the Roses are bare and the Delphiniums and

Phloxes have not pushed above ground, the border should even then be a blaze of beauty. Crocuses, Snowdrops, Aconites, and Primroses are quite enough for that purpose. The whole space under the Roses I should cover with the Common Wood Anemone and the Golden Wood Anemone, and early Cyclamens, and the earliest dwarf Daffodils. And among the Roses and Pæonies, and other medium-sized shrubs, I would put all the taller Lilies, such as Californian Lilies generally, the Japanese, Chinese, and finer American Lilies. Now we come to the front of the border, and here I would have combinations, such as the great St. Bruno's Lily and the delicate Hybrid Columbines, Primroses planted over hardy autumn Gladioli, so that when the Primroses are at rest the Gladioli should catch the eye. Carnations and Daffodils, planted so that the Carnations form a maze of blue-green for the delicate creams and oranges of the Daffodils. When the Daffodils are gone there are the Carnations in the autumn. A mass of Iberis correæfolia happens to have been the very best thing possible for some Lilium Browni to grow through, for the Iberis flowered early and then made a protection for the young growth of the Browni, and then a lovely dark green setting for the infinite beauty of the Lily flowers. As for saying that this cannot be done, I say that it is nonsense, for the Iberis flowered beautifully under such circumstances, and the Lilies too. If once you get into your head that no bit of ground ought ever to be seen without flowers or immediate prospect of flowers, heaps of combinations will immediately occur to those conversant with plants and the deep-rooting habits of most bulbs and the surface rooting of many herbaceous plants, for instance, Colchicums and Daffodils, with a surface of Campunula pusilla alba. The big leaves of the Colchicum grow

IN MY GARDEN
THIS MORNING

MARCH 22. Spring has begun in splendid fashion, but weather prophets foretell rain again shortly.

The scilla siberica (one of the few really blue flowers) is now blooming most beautifully. Each bulb produces several flower-stems, so that the display is spread over a long period.

The rock-cress is quickly covering itself with its dazzling white flowers. Purple buds now deck the aubrietia. Crocuses are just at their best.

Trumpet daffodils begin to greet one everywhere. Where there were only twelve flowers to be found a few days ago, fifty now are gleaming in the sunlight. The long winter days are over. Lucky are they who can greet spring in a lovely garden.

KELWAY'S "ARTISTIC" BORDERS

No. 6 "A." Kelway Pæony Border, composed of Kelway's lovely large flowered Pæonies. Per 100 Pæony plants (choice named kinds) from £10 or 20/- per 10 square yards; with bulbs between, 40/- per 10 square yards.

SOME people like the effect of a dark hedge of evergreen or other foliage at the back of their borders, but if there can be a choice between backgrounds a wall is better; and for edging, turf or native stone laid flat paviour-wise or on edge; do not choose edgings of box nor any formal plant edging, and certainly not tiles.

¶ As to soil, all soils grow some plant or other, so that for a special soil, special plants; and for special plants, a special soil; but for **general** borders—and they will be the basis or commencement of hardy perennial gardening, adding special beds and borders as convenient—a soil which will suit the general run of good kinds is advisable. Such a soil is, naturally, a "medium" one, neither heavy nor too light. If there is too much clay, loam and sand should be added; if too much sand, some heavy loam should be mixed in. Very much mulching of a border is not necessary after the first few months or when the border is well covered with small tufted plants in and around the bigger ones. The usefulness of mulching and of the growth of the small plants is to do away with too great evaporation; but the low-growing plants are preferable to the mulch in that they are beautiful and the mulch is not.

¶ Even when the soil of the garden is a "bad" soil, the wholesale importation of a "good soil" is not necessary, but the existing soil should be made the best of and improved, and we co-operate in this by leaving out of our Selections such plants as will not be likely to do well in particular soils.

¶ Our advice certainly is that no one be discouraged by the well-known remark, "Oh, you will never grow anything in this garden;" there are very few gardens like that, and, at any rate, strips can always be prepared fit for most hardy things. It is often the most unpromising garden which, after "spade-work" and intelligent attention, yields the best results. Neither must there be too keen a feeling of disappointment if the first year should not yield absolute perfection. The second and succeeding years may be looked for to give a very different and even surprisingly beautiful result.

---

in spring, and there would be nothing but leaves were it not for the masses of Daffodils. By-and-by the leaves of the Colchicums and Daffodils are dry enough to pull away, and then the Campanula, be it pusilla, pusilla alba, or turbinata alba, comes into a sheet of bloom. Before the bloom has passed away the Colchicums are 5 inches across, of the richest rose colour. I do not exactly feel that this is a colour-less kind of garden, and as I have a hundred different kinds of Daffodils, this little arrangement will not be without interest in spring.

The Daffodils and Colchicums root deeply and grow mostly in winter, requiring water then, and not in summer, when the Campanula carpet is taking it all. There are some, however, which one must be careful about—the common white Lily, for instance, which wants exposing to the sun in autumn. I do not mind the exquisite French Poppies among these Candidum Lilies, because the Poppies die about August, and then the Lilies get their baking and refuse to show the bare earth, soon covering it with all their leaves. For the extreme front of the border hundreds of combinations will occur—Pansies over Daffodils, Portulacas over Central Asian bulbs, Christmas Roses and Helebores over the taller Daffodils with Gladioli, Tritomas and giant Daffodils, Hepaticas, and autumn-blooming and spring-blooming Cyclamens, with Scillas and Snowdrops. When Anemone japonica is low, up come the taller Tulips, sylvestris, for instance, and higher still out of the dark green leaves come the bejewelled Crown Imperials.

As for the cultural advantages, I can imagine this system in the hands of a skilful gardener to be the best of all. In the first place, *the plants suffer much less from drought, because there is so much less surface exposed to sun and wind*. Examine, not right under the root, but under the spreading part of a mignonette, and see if, on a broiling hot day, the ground is not much cooler and moister than on the bare ground. Irises are almost the only plants I know of that do require the soil bare about their rootstocks; but then Irises are a carpet of green always, and a few clumps of Tiger Lilies or Tiger Irises will not seriously injure their flowering prospects. And what cannot be done with an herbaceous border edge when that edge is the green grass? The tiniest Scillas, and Hyacinths, and Daffodils, and Snowdrops, are leading into the border without any break. So, I believe, and I think many others will believe by-and-by, that every bulbous plant ought to be grown in combination with some-thing else, as Amaryllis Belladona, for instance, which I plant with Arum italicum pictum. In spring the Arum comes up extremely early, and its leaves protect the far more delicate leaves of the Amaryllis till they are growing freely and the Arum dies down. The ground is surfaced with Violets, so that the Belladonnas are coming into bloom, not with the bare ground, but with a setting of violet leaves in beautiful contrast with their pink blossoms. Christmas

KELWAY'S "ARTISTIC" BORDERS

No. 6 "B" May Flowering Pæonies, per 100 pæony plants £5, or 12/- per 10 square yards; with bulbs between, 30/- per 10 square yards.

IN MY GARDEN
THIS MORNING

APRIL 2. April, one of the sweetest months of the year, comes to find the garden by no means a barren waste. Indeed, March forestalled several of April's most treasured gifts.

On sunny days the bees gaily hum among the crocuses. Yet the beauty of these early flowers is fast passing away. Their bright appearance can be prolonged for a little by picking off the dead blossoms.

Quickly the hyacinths are opening. The hardy auriculas are also beginning to put forth their many-hued flowers. As they are almost as easy to grow as the popular polyanthus, they might with advantage be oftener seen in gardens.

WE find that people sometimes fight shy of certain plants, thinking they will not thrive with them because their native home is "Siberia" or "Africa," or because they are "alpines." There is no greater mistake. The larger portion of Siberia is far hotter for the greater part of the year than Britain, and some parts of Africa at certain altitudes are far colder ; but, again the question of elevation comes in, or rainfall, so that no plant should be "taboo" without real knowledge concerning its adaptability. Many alpines found in Switzerland at not less than 5,000 or 8,000 feet thrive gloriously in sunny Somerset at 300 feet ; it is not even absolutely necessary to remind them of their origin by building miniature imitations of the Matterhorn.

¶ *Nil desperandum* and *Experientia docet* should be the mottos for all gardeners. In the words of a fine gardener, recently dead, "You cannot tell what you can do with plants ; gardeners know very little about them really. Try ! I believe you will succeed if you intend to."

J. K.

Roses of all kinds would probably be a more beautiful setting still, but the Belladonnas want a good deal of summer drying up, which the Hellebores could not stand so well. . . . . *We have now a wealth of hardy plants, especially bulbs, which our forefathers never had,* and this combination of bulbous plants and herbaceous plants will certainly lead to a preparation of the borders which has been hardly dreamt of by people who do not care what they spend on tropical flowers ; for it seems to have been forgotten that we have Irises as big as a plate and Lilies as tall as a tree, all hardy and requiring little attention when once they have been properly planted. *The time that used to be spent year after year in digging acres of borders might now be spent in properly making or re-making a few yards of border,* till the whole outdoor borders are as exactly suited for the growth of plants to the utmost perfection—as many as possible being put in the given space—as the borders of a large conservatory. *It is in such a border as this that we attain the utmost variety, unceasingly beautiful, every yard different, every week varying, holding on its surface*

at least three times the value of plant life and successional plant beauty of any ordinary garden.—FRANK MILES.

No feature of the flower garden better expresses the latter-day development of gardening than the perennial border. In certain directions no firm of nurserymen has educated garden sentiment to a greater extent than Messrs. Kelway & Son, of Langport. *Morning Post.*

Extract from "The Garden," May 31st, 1913.

GROUPING FLOWERS FOR COLOUR.

The repeated requests for information and suggestion that have recently reached the Editor are a proof of the ever-increasing interest in the subject of grouping and arranging plants for colour effect. It is a significant sign of advance in the character of the aims of those who love their gardens. No one who has seen flower borders or other garden spaces well arranged for colour effect would ever go back to haphazard planting. A garden may contain an ample supply of the best plants, and the gardener may be the most able of cultivators, but if the plants are not placed to good effect it is only like having the best paints from the best colourman. In either case, it is only the exactly right use and right placing that will make the picture and in the case of flowers, show what they can really do for our most complete enjoyment.

G. JEKYLL.

IN MY GARDEN
THIS MORNING

APRIL 12. Mild, damp weather makes everything grow so quickly, and flowers open so suddenly that it is quite difficult to be up-to-date.

That splendid spring-flowering shrub, the pyrus japonica (the Japan quince), is now a lovely sight. Its deep scarlet flowers are very striking. It looks especially charming trained against a wall. Many shrubs can be grown in this manner, although they may not really be climbers.

Every lover of the country knows the marsh marigold, haunter of river banks. The double form of this plant thrives in the garden if given a damp position. Its brilliant yellow flowers are now opening.

KELWAY'S "ARTISTIC" BORDERS

No. 7. Kelway Delphinium Border. Those who have not seen Kelway's Delphiniums well-grown cannot imagine their wonderful loveliness. Per 100 plants (choice kinds), from £7 10s. 0d. per 100 ; 10 square yards from 20/-, 30/-, 40/- upwards.

SUGGESTIONS *for the* EQUIPMENT *of* LARGE BORDERS

❦

FOR long borders it is convenient sometimes to form a bay half-way down the border, and to place a garden seat therein, or in very long borders to repeat the seat at intervals. We have had two seats made, designs of which will be pleasing to those who are looking for simple effects in the garden.

¶ We call these the "Kelway" and the "Pæony" garden seats and offer them as illustrated, in deal, painted either white or green, at the prices on page 52. In many cases it will be thought best that the view should be carried uninterruptedly through the borders to a vista beyond, and for such cases we had had designed quadrant-shaped seats, which may be placed at the end, one on either side, each one facing the opposing border at an angle. The vista is then not interrupted and the borders can be admired separately and at leisure from the best position.

¶ When no value is attached to the non-interruption of the view these quadrant seats can be placed together, forming a semi-circular seat facing the whole length of the border. We can supply these seats as illustrated, in deal, painted white or green, at prices on page 52.

The MIXED *or* HERBACEOUS BORDER

An Appreciation of Messrs. Kelway & Son's Work. From the "Gardeners' Magazine."

On more than one occasion we have visited the nurseries of Messrs. Kelway & Son at Langport, Somerset, and never without gaining fresh knowledge from those, to the horticulturist and farmer, intensely interesting acres. One phase of the work especially appealed to us—the well-thought out schemes of colour for the mixed border, and no season is more appropriate than the present for considering this delightful feature--or should be—of the English garden.

There is no more trustworthy teacher to those who wish for both sumptuous and refined effects in the garden than Miss Jekyll. We take the following from her well-known book, "Colour in the Garden." In the introduction is summed up the best advice that can be given on this interesting phase of English gardening, as undertaken with the best results by Messrs. Kelway.

"To plant and maintain a flower-border, **with a good scheme for colour,** is by no means the easy thing that is commonly supposed. I believe that the way in which it can be made successful is to devote certain borders to certain times of the year; each border or garden requires to be bright from one to three months. Nothing seems to me more unsatisfactory than the border that in spring shows a few patches of flowering bulbs in ground otherwise looking empty, or with tufts of herbaceous plants just coming through. Then the bulbs die down and their place is wanted for something that comes later. Either the ground will then show bare patches, or the place of the bulbs will be forgotten, and they will be cruelly stabbed by fork or trowel when it is wished to put something in the apparently empty space. . . .

I am strongly of opinion that the possession of a quantity of plants, however good the plants may be themselves and however ample their number, does not make a garden; it only makes a **collection.** Having got the plants, the great thing is to use them with careful selection and definite intention. Merely having them, or having them planted unassorted in garden spaces, is only like having a box of paints from the best colourman, or, to go one step further, it is like having portions of these paints set out upon a palette. This does not constitute a picture, and it seems to me that the duty we owe to our gardens, and to our own bettering in our gardens, is so to use the plants that they shall form beautiful pictures, and that, while delighting our eyes, they should be always training those eyes to a more exalted criticism, to a state of mind and artistic conscience that will not tolerate bad or careless combination or any sort of misuse

KELWAY'S "ARTISTIC" BORDERS

No. 8. Kelway Lupine Border. Composed of hybrid Lupines, white, yellow, lilac, purple and blue. Price on application.

IN MY GARDEN THIS MORNING

APRIL 23. Spring continues her triumphant progress in spite of bitter days.

The nightingale is heard on still evenings, swift-winged swallows dart to and fro in the April sunshine. The white rock-cress (arabis albida) is as indispensable to the spring garden as the daffodil. It is now a carpet of pure white. The double form is also beautiful, its wiry-stemmed flowers being useful for picking. Forget-me-nots, quickly following the scillas and "glory of the snow," begin to surround many a bed with a haze of delicate blue. Grape-hyacinths, grown in masses, now look very charming. The variety "heavenly blue" certainly does not belie its name.

FOLLOWING an old-fashioned and very delightful custom, many place a sundial or low stone seat (circular in shape) half-way between one end of their Double Herbaceous Borders and the other. This addition, with flagged walks and cross walk, by no means detracts from the beauty of the borders. It adds an element of formality which, although it is not our own ideal, is in accordance with the taste of many.

¶ There is nothing so good as a background for Herbaceous Borders as a stone wall—a well-built old one for choice. Many brick walls are almost equally handsome. It is not necessary in every aspect to have a background at all, and in many instances one may prefer that there should be none.

¶ There are, however, cases where a background is either necessary or desired, and where stone or brick walls are neither desirable nor possible. In such cases rather than plant Privet, Laurel, Box or Yew, we would recommend Treillage of a simple design, and of the many designs we have seen the one we illustrate on page 51 is simple and suitable.

---

of plants, but in which it becomes a point of honour to be always striving for the best. It is just in the way it is done that lies the whole difference between commonplace gardening and gardening that may rightly claim to rank as a fine art. Given the same space of ground and material, they may either be fashioned into a dream of beauty, a place of perfect rest and refreshment of mind and body—a series of soul-satisfying pictures—a treasure of well-set jewels ; or they may be so misused that everything is jarring and displeasing. To learn how to perceive the difference and how to do right is to apprehend gardening as a fine art. In practice it is to place every plant or group of plants with such thoughtful care and definite intention that they shall form a part of a harmonious whole, and that successive portions, or, in some cases, even single details, shall show a series of pictures. It is so to regulate the trees and undergrowth of the wood that their lines and masses come into beautiful form and harmonious proportion ; it is to be always watching, noting and doing, and putting oneself into closest acquaintance and sympathy with the growing things."

The first thing to think of when establishing a border is

**IN MY GARDEN
THIS MORNING**

MAY 3. The splendour of triumphant youth fills the garden. No sign of decay is to be seen anywhere. Even in the wood unrolling fern fronds and the deepening blue of the bluebells have hidden last year's dead leaves.

Christmas roses are densely covered with young green, while the crocus leaves still look cheerful. Where the old foliage was removed from the ivy its fresh verdant growth begins to brighten wall and bower again.

The dark garden ways are now flooded with the nightingales' song. Long after the "witching time" they sing. The quaint notes of the cuckoo grow more familiar every day. "The sun, the sun!" is the longing cry of bird and flower.

the soil, and it must not be forgotten that perennial plants make heavy demands, necessitating, if they are to fulfil their rightful mission—that of imparting rich colouring wherever they are placed—a thoroughly well-prepared border, enriched with manure. Much depends upon situation and the natural character of the soil. The writer has some difficulty in maintaining the full vigour of the plants because the soil is naturally the lightest of gravels, and a depth of 2 ft. to 3 ft. of a prepared mixture was necessary in the first place, with an annual dressing of well-decayed manure. Soil of an opposite nature does not require this assistance, and, from the writer's experience, the plants are less given to spreading far and wide, such as the perennial sunflowers are prone to do, with the loss of vigour, wealth, and size of the flowers.

We have carefully studied the planting plans that are given by Messrs. Kelway and have nothing but praise for the excellent attempt that has been made to grapple with this vexed gardening question—that of obtaining the right association of colour from the hardy perennials. We have seen the result in the Langport nursery, a lovely mixed border having been planted for many years as an object-lesson in using this class with a definite scheme in the mind's eye. There are not only what is called the "Artistic Permanent General Border," but those of flowers for the four seasons of the year, with much practical information upon the making of borders that are to be filled with one kind of plant—Pæony, Delphinium, Michaelmas Daisy or perennial Aster, and bulbs. A border of well-established Pæonies with a background of dark-leaved shrubs to throw into rich relief the many shades of colour is very reminiscent. And all who have visited the Langport nursery in the

KELWAY'S "ARTISTIC" BORDERS

No. 9. Kitchen Garden Flower Border. Estimate at moderate rates on application.

BEAUTIFUL INDEED AND YET SO SIMPLE.

time of the Pæony will remember that wonderful scene—acres of plants in the full zenith of their beauty, single and double, displaying an exquisite range of colours from snow white to darkest crimson, and filling the air with a sweet scent. The writer has never seen a gayer panorama of beauty, which starts with the deep crimson shoots in spring, then the beautiful mature leaf and remarkable splendour from the expanded bloom. These words are true also of the Delphinium or perennial Larkspur, with which the name of Kelway will be for all time associated ; and a border planted now with strong tufts of the finest varieties will prove a great boon next summer. March and early April are the months to plant the perennials, but the earlier the better, in case keen winds and dryness are experienced, which tells much against the welfare of the flowers.

It has always been the object of Messrs. Kelway to obtain good colours. No matter whether it is the Gladiolus, Delphinium, Pæony or the annual flower, nothing is allowed to exist that is not " artistic " from the standpoint of colour, and this the planter of the border must remember. It is in the grouping of decided shades that the richest pictures are produced, and this is shown by such an illustration as accompanies these remarks. The first year the border will not have reached its full beauty, but there need be no want of colour when one has the great family of annual flowers to draw upon—Sweet Peas, the exquisite shades among the

Ostrich Plume China Asters, and also the finest in colour among the many exotics that may be raised from seed. The writer has written of the borders for all seasons, but in doing so is not forgetful of the general features of these beautiful acres near the old Somerset town.

In no trade is there a more praiseworthy readiness to devote a large proportion of time and money to public helpfulness than in the professions allied to gardening. As evidences of public spiritedness in business work, may be cited the interesting publications issued by many nurserymen and seedsmen of repute. These have, of course, as chief aim the promotion of trade, but in the pursuits of floriculture, enthusiasm oft seizes the man of business and turns him into preacher, teacher, and propagandist before he is aware of the metamorphosis he is undergoing.

KELWAY'S "ARTISTIC" BORDERS

No. 10. A North Border, for Spring. Price on application.

IN MY GARDEN
THIS MORNING

MAY 14. Everything is growing at a wonderful rate. In a few days another act in the garden drama will commence early summer.

Pæonies, crowned with massive buds, soon will be flowering. Columbines, rockets, lupins, need but another burst of sunshine. The well-known saxifrage, London Pride, has sent up its ruddy stems and the pretty little blooms begin to open. It is one of the easiest plants to grow, being at home in sun or shade, poor soil or good.

Yet one's thoughts turn ever from the flowers to trees. Larches, elms, beeches, gleaming against the blue sky, are pictures to be lingered over.

15

HERBACEOUS BORDER AND PERGOLA.

Messrs. Kelway & Sons, the well-known nurserymen, are examples of this truth. They have created at Langport, in Somerset, gardens of their own which are renowned throughout the Kingdom. Their catalogues are works of art and interest, and they add to these trade publications the issue of a "Manual of Horticulture," and a pamphlet bearing the title which heads this paragraph "Gardens of Delight."

☙

A BEAUTIFUL ENGLISH NURSERY

Last July we spent several instructive and interesting hours in the beautiful nursery of Messrs. Kelway & Son, of Langport. Some years had elapsed since we previously made acquaintance with these broad acres—about 300 under cultivation—near the quaint old Somerset town. The Pæonies and Delphiniums were in full beauty, and Messrs. Kelway are famous all the world over for these two glorious summer flowers ; but there were acres of Gladioli and Sweet Peas, and, in fact, no phase of horticulture seemed unrepresented. It is impossible to name a tithe of the things to be seen. No matter what the season may be, there is always something to interest one here—in winter the exotics under glass, and from Daffodil-time until the frost there are the hardy flowers and the vegetables to inspect, and the best forms in the various sections to be noted. One was impressed with the perfect keeping of the nursery, although so vast in extent. From the pretty English garden surrounding Mr. James Kelway's home—Wearne Wyche—with its wealth of roses and hardy flowers, to the furthermost part of the nursery there is something to see and admire. The approach to the nursery is by a shady walk bordered by ferns and wild flowers, and then the Pæonies and the Delphiniums which have contributed so largely to the reputation of Messrs. Kelway, break in on the view. It is impossible to describe the effect of the groups of one variety, set out, of course, as one would expect in a nursery, but teaching the lesson that in massing certain varieties a rare picture of colour is obtained. The ground is undulating in parts, the little valleys are smothered in bloom, and the air is filled with perfume.

IN MY GARDEN
THIS MORNING

MAY 24. The beauty and charm of the garden are now so wonderful that it is quite impossible to describe them. One can tell of the countless lovely flowers, the fresh green of everything, but the knowledge that it is not always May, that it is May now, fills one's heart with a sweet joy beyond the power of words.

Bluebells in wood and garden have laid a "heavenly carpet on the ground." There is a pink "bluebell" (scilla hispanica) that is just as easy to grow and has large flowers.

Distant fields are yellow with the mustard.

Weed though it be, the country would lose a May charm if this common thing did not gleam in the sunshine.

KELWAY'S "ARTISTIC" BORDERS

No. 11. A South Border, for full sun. Price on application.

BORDER WITH WALL BACKGROUND.

"Many of the hardy flowers we treasure for their beauty have been raised at Langport, and to give a list and descriptions would fill a large volume."

The Ladies' Field.

HERBACEOUS BORDERS

"The best characteristic of English gardening is found in the splendour of perennial herbaceous borders as designed by Kelway & Son, the Langport experts. The firm were awarded a Gold Medal at the Franco-British Exhibition for their marvellous display of pretty blooms.

"All who take any interest in gardening, both from the æsthetic and horticultural point of view, must fully appreciate the attitude adopted during the last dozen or so years by that old-fashioned firm, Messrs. Kelway & Son, of Langport, Somerset. There was always a craze for the cultivation of rare, exotic, hot-house and certain well-known plants, but Messrs. Kelway & Son have been great leaders in a much better movement, and one within the reach of all who possess even the smallest patch of ground. A glance at their Manual—as their sumptuous catalogue is called, the possession of which is a never-failing joy to its owner from its artistic merits, quite apart from the fund of information

to be gleaned from its pages—shows us at once how much we are indebted to the firm for the improvements in certain groups of plants."

Ladies' Field.

"The plans formed by Kelways will ensure a never-ceasing beauty of bloom in our borders through spring, autumn, and summer, and even in the depths of winter berry and evergreens will remain to cheer us. Kelways have made an earnest study of colour effect. It is very dolorous to see one's borders bare and colourless for perhaps a month at a time between the seasons, and by following carefully thought-out plans of Messrs. Kelway this unpleasant barrenness may be altogether avoided."

The Tatler.

IN MY GARDEN
THIS MORNING

JUNE 4. If a rose is the queen of summer flowers, then assuredly the pæony is their king. Pæonies, for massive display and splendid colouring, are unrivalled. To-day many of the tightly folded buds have burst.

The double-red is the best known variety, but there are countless others having pink to crimson, white, and yellow flowers (many sweet-scented) which are much more beautiful. The coppery-coloured foliage of some pæonies is very charming by way of contrast to the bright green of others.

Single forms are especially good for picking, and ought to be better known. House martins and swallows are now busy under overhanging eaves, the muddy village-pond hard by providing their building material.

KELWAY'S "ARTISTIC" BORDERS

No. 12. A Colour Border of Annual Flowers, from seed. For about 20 yards by 3 yards 25/-, or a double border 45/-

THE accompanying suggestions for the effective planting of herbaceous borders are worth careful reading. They embody the experiences of masters of the craft and the ideas of experts who are also enthusiasts.

Gardeners' Magazine.

ø

A JULY BORDER

The portion of flower border shown in the accompanying illustration is in the garden of Mr. Walter Jesper, Beechwood, Menston-in-Wharfedale, Yorkshire, who kindly sent us the photograph and the following notes: "The photograph was taken when the border was at its height of beauty, *i.e.*, about the second week in July. The flowers just showing at the bottom right-hand corner are Campanulas. High above them is the splendid Delphinium Reynaldo. Between this and the Cupressus is the beautiful creamy Delphinium Beauty of Langport, which shows to great advantage against the dark foliage behind. Just below is a young plant of D. Balladonna, in front of which rise the handsome, tall leaves of Iris Monnieri, not yet in bloom. Below this is a spike of the white Mallow, while on the stone edging are Saxifrages and the charming little Campanulas pusilla and pusilla alba. In the centre of the picture, just to the left of Delphinium Beauty of Langport, are the graceful spikes of Anchusa italica Opal. Beyond is an old-established plant of the early-flowering white Phlox, and near the edge of the border is a group of Veronica spicata alba. Further groups of Delphiniums are seen in the background. Altogether, the effect of this long border (some 12 feet wide) in what we call our "blue fortnights" in July, is one that lingers long in the memory, even when winter is upon us.

The Garden.

A KELWAY JULY BORDER.
Published in "The Garden," March 29th, 1913.

ø

GRADATION

The last of the laws of colour we may consider is that of gradation, and the flowers themselves show the beauty of gradation in a manner in which no words could ever do. Examine a fine rose, and observe the shading in the various petals, and you have at once one of the finest object lessons on gradation that can be had. Gradation in the garden is as the finishing touch to a good picture. It gives charm and finish, and a note of refinement wherever shown.

This, then, in brief is a summary of the guiding principles in colour combination in the garden. An assiduous practice of these principles, even in their simple forms, will amply repay garden lovers.

Amateur Gardening.

IN MY GARDEN
THIS MORNING

JUNE 14. The petals from the dark blue German irises have fallen, but here are mauve, white, pale blue flags to take their places. These later varieties should be as widely grown as the well-known early one, as their culture is of the simplest.

Bright yellow day-lilies, rising from a mass of wavy foliage, are now some of the most beautiful flowers in the garden. Though each blossom is short-lived, as its name implies, every stalk has a large number of buds.

KELWAY'S "ARTISTIC" BORDERS

No. 13. A Border for Small Gardens in Towns. Price on application.

REVIVAL *in* HARDY PLANTS

From *Gardeners' Magazine.*

THE commencement of the revival of interest in hardy plants takes us back about forty years, and a reference thereto recalls to mind many pleasant incidents in connection therewith. Possibly some of those who read these notes may consider that a later date would possibly be more correct. It must, however, be remembered that this revival, with its far-reaching effects, did not have its genesis coincident with the time when owners of gardens and those engaged in their management, began to buy and plant hardy perennials in considerable quantities. Such activities were a manifest proof that a great change was being made; but we have to go back some years anterior thereto for the purpose of finding the initiation of the work that rendered the revival possible. There had to be some years of persistent advocacy of the claims that hardy plants had upon all who were concerned with the decorative aspects of the garden, before any considerable portion of them could be diverted from the various tender plants that had for many years been regarded with such favour. Moreover, some thirty-five years or so ago so little was known of the finest of the hardy plants that much educational work had to be accomplished before any material change could, with success, be effected. In this work the *Gardeners' Magazine* rendered valuable service in various directions.

HARDY PLANT IMPROVEMENT

Another important factor was the splendid service rendered by those members of the trade who had never lost their faith in them, but had continued the improvement of some of the kinds throughout the period in which the interest in hardy flowers was at its lowest ebb. For example, Mr. William Kelway had become greatly interested in the herbaceous pæonies before the massing of tender bedding plants in the flower garden had made such progress, and, gathering up all the most meritorious varieties he could obtain, he went steadily on with his work in improving the form and increasing the size of the flowers and developing new shades of colour. In this he achieved a high degree of success, and by his example induced others to take up the work of cross-fertilisation, some of the most noteworthy achievements being such distinct and beautiful varieties as Exquisite, Lady Curzon, Lady of the West, and Lord Rosebery. Some years later the pyrethrums were taken

THE NEW WATER LILIES.
See Kelway's Manual.

KELWAY'S "ARTISTIC" BORDERS

No. 14. Kelway April Border. Price as for Nos. 1 "A" and 1 "B."

IN MY GARDEN THIS MORNING

JUNE 25. Hot sunshine, moist soil, what more could the most fastidious summer flower long for? Violas and pansies are more beautiful than ever. Rose-beds, planted thickly with violas of one colour, are now a wonderful sight.

Early varieties of lychnis (campion) light the garden with crimson fires, while, with its softer hue, valerian towers around. Spanish irises will soon be in full bloom, and no flowers are more charming grown in mild masses. Blue, yellow, white—all are lovely. Early gladioli also tempt one to songs of praise.

To-day the orchard hedges are still bright with wild roses, beloved even at this season of splendour.

WALL GARDEN.

in hand by Mr. Kelway, and, as the result of this pioneer work, large collections of flowers were exhibited both at South Kensington and Regent's Park, and these assisted in obtaining for hardy plants the attention that had for so long a period been denied them. *Gardeners' Magazine.*

❦

OPPORTUNITIES MISSED IN PUBLIC GARDENS

Extracted from "The Architectural Review," June, 1909.

"I do hold it," Bacon writes, "in the royal ordering of gardens there ought to be gardens for all the months of the year, in which, severally, things of beauty may be then in season." All this "that you may have *ver perpetuum* as the place affords." This is for the prince's garden; but anyone may contrive an herbaceous border, so arranged and planted that something like a perpetual spring is the result.

That a continual procession of flowers through the climbing months is gained is nothing if the colours are not carefully chosen and blended. With a little care and with the help of a skilful gardener, there should be little trouble about realising it.

The roses are come, most beautiful of English flowers, to fill gardens with delight, to entwine the simple trellis of green galleries with leaves and tendrils and hang it with blossoms red and white; to fill bowers with their flowers and make the air heavy with their perfume. But of this it seems the gardeners have no knowledge. While the cottager has his porch a mass of roses, his simple garden filled with the old-fashioned flowers—a blaze of harmonious colour—the London County Council fill their parks with patchwork flower-beds for all the world like those old garish mid-Victorian patchwork coverlets. Their gardeners are no doubt skilful and accurate—indeed the precision with which their bedding-out is done is perfectly appalling. Like rows of soldiers they stand, three or four red tulips, then the same number of yellow ones, then those of a magenta colour, followed by some of hybrid persuasion, and perhaps a tail of white ones. The next regiment is composed of

IN MY GARDEN THIS MORNING

July 5. Here are the lovely sweet peas, perhaps the most welcome of summer flowers. Growing on either side of a long gravel path, they will soon form two great hedges of bloom, and what a joy a walk between them will be in the early morning!

The most brilliant colour now in the garden is presented by the scarlet lychnis, a splendid plant that will light up a whole border.

Lily-time has begun. To-day, from their moist quarters, the early varieties of this beautiful family, with yellow, orange, and scarlet blossoms, proudly raise their heads. The white Madonna lilies, the fairest of all, will soon scent the hot July air.

KELWAY'S "ARTISTIC" BORDERS

No. 15. Kelway May Border. Price as for No. 1 "A" and No. 1 "B."

ALPINE BORDER OR ROCK GARDEN.

wallflowers, first red, then mixed, then yellow, and so on. They pursue all sorts of evolutions, sometimes perfectly straight, sometimes curved, in a clump here at random, there a single flower has fallen out from the ranks. All is thoughtless or worse; bad taste is here as rampant as in our streets, although it cannot quite take away the beauty of the flowers themselves.

The beds have no form or arrangement; they meander about, the flowers set at regular intervals, and their species changed every six feet or so without any idea of design or sense of colour. The aristocratic rose looks down despondingly on a patch of bare earth or across at a fellow placed some feet away.

Geraniums feel self-conscious in their isolation. The red and yellow striped tulips make a noise like the horrid bounders they are. This is not as it should be; instead of waiting till public opinion makes it uncomfortable for their gardeners, the County Council should take thought and mend.

When the "garden suburbs" are being planned in some order, with greens and gardens, when interest is awakening in their arrangement and in garden literature, it is time for public bodies to make a step forward.

Where are the old-fashioned flowers: Columbines, Sweet Williams, Cowslips, London Pride, Forget-Me-Not, Marigold, Mignonette, and all the hosts of lovely, lowly blossoms? They are too common and quiet for the modern gardener, whose idea is to get loud patches of colour unrelated to anything else in the garden. The effect is like that of a brass band playing delicate melodies on the drums and trombones.

One of the pleasantest ways of setting flowers is in a long border. To the appreciation of its full beauty it should be seen end on and should be arranged to this end, and may with advantage be of great length. The great border at Hampton Court, along the east front, will occur to everyone; it is about a quarter of a mile long and some six feet wide. It is planted against a fine brick wall. Lowly flowers at the edge mount to taller and gorgeous ones at the back. The effect is splendid and there can be no finer sight than this glowing mass of colour set against the old weather-beaten wall of brick and stone.

KELWAY'S "ARTISTIC" BORDERS

No. 16.   Kelway June Border.   Prices as for No. 1 "A" and No. 1 "B."

IN MY GARDEN
THIS MORNING

JULY 16.   Summer is at its height. Looking out from among the cool shadows of the pines, the noontide garden appears a veritable blaze of colour.

Phloxes are some of the most brilliant of our hardy flowers. Words cannot describe the gorgeous effect of bold clumps when freely blooming.

The earliest varieties are now coming out. The dwarf phloxes (one to two feet high) are just as pretty as the tall growing species.

Another beautiful family of plants beginning to flower are the sedums (stonecrops). The common yellow wall-pepper is perhaps their most widely known representative.

KITCHEN GARDEN BORDER.

There is no reason at all why similar arrangements should not be made in our public gardens. It is convenient to have great paths leading straight through the gardens and herbaceous borders could be arranged on each side. Gravel should be substituted for asphalt, and a pleasant addition to all would be a fountain, giving a centre to the whole. This in a town would not be a costly affair, and nothing is pleasanter to the senses than the play of a jet of water among trees and flowers. *Architectural Review.*

"IN EVERY MONTH FLOWERS"

From "Amateur Gardening."

One of the most remarkable features of the modern hardy garden is the way in which the very skill with which

IN MY GARDEN
THIS MORNING

JULY 26. There are many plants, which, though easy to grow and attractive, have no common English names. This has quite a frightening effect on some people, who prefer to cultivate flowers bearing titles familiar to all.

Many may not have heard of montbretias, those pretty bulbs from South Africa, with little yellow or red flowers on wiry stalks. To-day they are beginning to bloom.

Flower-stems quickly appear on the gladioli, perhaps the most gorgeous subjects August and September bring. Thus summer (at least to the gardener) is passing. Autumn's flowers, crowned with buds, greet us everywhere.

they are arranged is concealed. The quest of the garden ideal of to-day has not driven art from the garden. On the contrary, it realises the true art that conceals its ways and means. The beautiful schemes of colour please the eye by the broadness of their effect, and not by any apparent details.

In the Kelway Artistic Herbaceous Border this revival reaches the zenith of its achievements. Indeed, its very existence owes more, perhaps, to the Kelways than to any others who have made the hardy garden their life work. To realise in some measure the study they must have given to this glorious object, one has only to think of the main features of a Kelway garden.

The most important is the placing of the flowers with regard to their colour effect. Harmony is the rule. The eye is continually delighted with splendid harmonies of rich and brilliant colour and proper sequences of such harmonies. Each mass of colour, although large enough to be distinctive and characteristic, is never overbearing, and although a Kelway Border includes all the colours of the garden, the warm gay scarlets, crimsons, oranges and yellow, never clash with delicate tints of purple or lilac.

The gradation of heights is also an important point to be observed. From the majestic towering Delphinium to the daintiest little flower that tumbles over the edge of the bed, the disposition of heights, when considered in conjunc-

KELWAY'S "ARTISTIC" BORDERS

No. 17. Kelway July Border. Price as for No. 1 "A" and No. 1 "B."

GYPSOPHILA PANICULATA—A BEAUTIFUL HARDY BORDER PLANT.

tion with the effects secured by the colour scheme, is a triumph of horticultural skill.

Then there is that glorious feature of the Kelway Garden which serves as a title for our article, " In Every Month Flowers." From the first fresh shoots of early spring until the frost comes round again, there are abundant flowers in a Kelway Garden. A poet has called flowers, " stars that in earth's firmament do shine." His simile is rendered beautifully apt by the succession of bloom that appears in a Kelway Garden. Like as we gave into the firmament above as the darkness gathers in density, and the beads of light appear one after the other, now in the east, now in the west, until the whole arc of sky is bejewelled with them, so in a Kelway Garden the buds burst into flower with delightful unexpectedness and gathering glory. Here is no pattern that has its day and then gives place to another. But as each week brings into season its contribution of colour and bloom, so the scheme unfolds and gathers character, an ever-changing and always delightful picture to the eye.

How happy, too, is one who has access to a hardy garden, in the profusion of flowers always available for cutting. Fully fifty per cent. of the flowers in a Kelway Garden are eminently suitable for indoor decoration, yielding an always fresh and ever liberal supply.

It is obvious that to bring the hardy garden to its present

successful state Messrs. Kelway & Son have had to give minute attention to the cultivation and improvement of hundreds of plants. There are certain plants with which the firm have effected such wonders that the name of Kelway has become inseparably associated with them. Who that knows the twentieth century Pæony, Delphinium, Pyrethrum, or Gaillardia, can think of them without dwelling with pleasure on what Kelways have done for those now leading subjects of the hardy garden? Let us glance at these four subjects individually.

The Pæony is a Kelway plant **par excellence.** The difference between a Kelway Pæony and the kinds which were cultivated in this country before Messrs. Kelway took the Pæony in hand is immense. But since these scientific nurserymen took them up, they have gained wonderfully in

IN MY GARDEN
THIS MORNING

AUGUST 6. As summer passes, many sights in the garden turn our thoughts to the future. Yews, firs, laurels, now fully decked with their new verdure, seem to speak of the last dark days of the year, the days when they will comfort us.

Many flowers must be grown in masses if their beauty is to be fully appreciated. A large clump of hyacinthuses (easily grown bulbs with pendulous white blossoms) is now a charming picture, as also is a clump of wild harebells on the rockery.

KELWAY'S "ARTISTIC" BORDERS

No. 18. Kelway August Border. Price as for No. 1 "A" and No. 1 "B."

A Kelway Border.

A Kelway Border.—The Fresh Beauty of the Early Year.

grace of floral form, in variety and richness of colour. They are very welcome for giving a dash of brilliance to our gardens between spring and summer, and there is hardly any position in which they may not be grown with striking effect.

Running the Pæony very closely as the most improved plant of the century is the Delphinium. The blue of a Delphinium is always pleasing in a garden, even when the flowers are on the comparatively puny and thinly blossomed spikes of the old varieties. So what shall we say of the exquisite tints in the many varieties from Langport? The spikes are long and thickly set with broad open flowers, in shades ranging from the fresh azure of the Forget-Me-Not to the depth of sapphire and the hue of imperial purple. Their majestic heights ensure Kelway's Delphiniums being prominent in any garden scheme in which they are included, but we particularly like to see them in broad masses with a background of trees in the distance, when the mass of beautiful blue gains wonderfully in intensity. We cannot do without Kelway's beautiful blue Delphiniums.

Reference was made above to the abundance of flowers for cutting afforded by the Kelway Garden, and among the chief contributors to this happy advantage are Kelway's improved Pyrethrums. There is something fascinating to the artistic eye in the elegance of a single Pyrethrum. And how they have been improved in form, size, colours, and

general beauty! Their chief beauty is seen in May and June, and for many weeks flowers succeed flowers without stint. Then the Gaillardia, last to be selected particularly from among the many Kelway plants, has had a very rapid march forward. No flowers in the border are more showy or last longer, and their value is never more appreciated than in times of drought, when they show scarcely any signs of flagging. The Kelway range of Gaillardias includes many varieties, and a Kelway Gaillardia, with flowers five inches in diameter, is by no means an unusual sight. They are amongst those hardy perennials that give abundant blossom the same year as planted.

We cannot leave our particularising without mentioning Kelway's hybrid Lupines, which give us many new delicate shades, and improved Phloxes and Gladioli.

IN MY GARDEN
THIS MORNING

August 16. When the next full moon lamps the sky it will look down on fading flowers and paths strewn with the first autumn leaves.

Last night, the garden, gay with every August blossom, was a fairy place after sunset.

The dew, so good for the dahlias and gladioli, grows heavier each clear night, while steamy mists begin to roam the valleys! Even now, one notices a darker hue creeping over the woods, but the proud purple of the heather hills drives sorrowful thoughts away.

KELWAY'S "ARTISTIC" BORDERS

No. 19. Kelway September Border. Price as for No. 1 "A" and No. 1 "B."

A KELWAY BORDER.—BETWIXT SPRING AND SUMMER.

Those are some of the aristocracy of the Kelway Herbaceous Border. Now a word about the scheme as applicable to one's individual wants. As shown above, an intimate knowledge of hundreds of plants and a faultless taste for arrangement and colour effects, are necessary before one can have a wholly successful hardy garden—one that will give "in every month flowers." But these conditions need not deter any garden lover who lacks the qualifications from having such a garden. Kelway & Son make a speciality of applying their unique scheme to any extent of soil, and are as willing to advise regarding the filling of a small garden as to submit estimates for laying out a park. The first thing to be done is to give them particulars of the space to be filled, such as dimensions, soil, and position. With these before them they make a selection of their improved hardy plants

based on the Kelway Artistic Herbaceous Border scheme, and submit the list with an estimate to the prospective customer. On approval of their suggestions, the plants are packed, labelled, and arranged in order ready for planting, with full instructions, so that everything that can be done to ensure success is done.   *Amateur Gardening.*

The BLUE GARDEN

"Come and see my 'Blue Garden,'" was an invitation which rather puzzled me several years ago; but when the spot was reached the mystery was solved. It was a lovely day in April—a day that made one forget that cold east winds still blow and chilling rain falls before summer comes. We had walked along the wide grass pathway between borders where many varieties of Daffodils and Narcissus were still in golden, lemon, and white masses, the soft west breeze laden with their fragrance. The brilliant green of the Crown Imperial (Fritillaria imperialis), like miniature palms, encircled by an orange whorl of buds, stood in the background, while overhead on the arched pergola the fresh leaves of the pillar and rambler roses intermingled with the greyish green tints of the early Clematis. The path seem to terminate in a high box hedge, but turning to the left we passed through a narrow entrance in this wall of green and entered the inner shrine.

IN MY GARDEN
THIS MORNING

SEPTEMBER 6. Few plants are now more brilliant than the cardinal flower lobelias. Their intense scarlet blossoms and purplish leaves are exceedingly beautiful. Though apt to die during the winter on wet soils, in many gardens they prove quite hardy.

Fine blooms are no longer found on the sweet peas, yet, because of their perfume, one is loth to cut them down.

Tall nasturtiums still deck many fences with gay flowers. If allowed to seed themselves, they will appear year after year, even though (in the process of digging) the seed should become buried more than a foot deep.

KELWAY'S "ARTISTIC" BORDERS

No. 20. Kelway October Border. Price as for No. 1 "A" and 1 "B."

A KELWAY BORDER IN EARLY MAY.

It was a space some thirty feet square. On three sides was the close-cut box hedge, broken only by the narrow passage. On the fourth side was a high grey stone wall, over the top of which peeped the branches of an apple tree, with swollen buds which would soon burst into rosy beauty. This wall was covered with the glossy dark green leaves of the Ceanothus, the flowers just beginning to show their lovely pale blue under-tint. At the foot of the wall a white wooden garden seat was placed, flanked on either side by rockwork. On the centre of the newly-mown lawn stood an old sundial, with the legend " I mark none but sunny hours." All round this emerald sward was a border from eight feet to ten feet wide, and this border was blue. Blues of every shade, from the deepest indigo and royal, purest cobalt and softest China, to the clearest azure, blended together, and one wondered if anything so beautiful had been seen before.

The Scillas were almost over, but their fading brilliance was kindly screened by Forget-Me-Not. The Chionodoxas and Grape Hyacinths were still masses of beauty, with tall porcelain and indigo Hyacinths in groups behind. The small blue Anemone dropped its bell-shaped head, and the blue Primrose, curious and unreal, looked up with its bright yellow eye. Over the rockwork, the cobalt flowers of the French Forget-Me-Not shone from every crevice, smothering the copper-tinted tendrils of the Lithospermum, while the whole groundwork of the border was a blue sea, with wave-like masses of various Forget-Me-Nots, above which rose the pale green shoots of Lupines, Delphiniums, and Monkshoods—giving promise of future beauty. It was my first introduction to a blue garden, and as I stood revelling in the loveliness of the rich colouring, several fantail pigeons came fluttering down with all the assurance of welcome pets, their snow-white plumage contrasting with their surroundings like glistening sails on a sunlit ocean.

There are so many true blue herbaceous plants and bulbs, as well as annuals and biennials, that can be cheaply procured and easily grown, that a collection can be made without going to great expense, and except during the few mid-winter weeks, a blue blossom will brighten the dull earth and gladden the eye. In a " one-colour " garden the essential thing to be remembered is that the various

KELWAY'S "ARTISTIC" BORDERS

No. 20. Kelway Michaelmas Daisy Border.   Price on application.

IN MY GARDEN
THIS MORNING

SEPTEMBER 17. Buds are discernable on the Christmas roses. This should remind us that, unless we take heed, they will be almost the only flowers to gather when winter grips the garden.

Now is the time when violets (for winter flowering) should be carefully lifted and planted in a cold frame close to the glass. If abundant air is given them and healthy frosts are guarded against, we shall be able to pick many a sweet bunch of these welcome blossoms throughout the year's dark days.

Violets may also be planted in sheltered positions in the open, for providing early flowers.

A KELWAY BORDER.—JULY OF THE FIRST YEAR.

shades and plants require to be grown in clumps and wide breadths, for if dotted singly, the whole will present a confused mass. Too many straight lines, circles, or squares should be avoided. Instead of a set design the plants should be grouped in irregular "patch-work" like masses, with care and knowledge as to height and tone of colour, so that the whole may become one harmonious mosaic of form and shade.

COLOUR PRINCIPLES

Whenever a mixed bed or border is tried, colour principles ought to be followed. These principles I wish to outline in as concise a manner as is possible, and in simple language.

IN MY GARDEN
THIS MORNING

SEPTEMBER 27. The wonderful violas are still blooming. For more than four months these indispensable plants have been smothered with refined, yet showy flowers.

Although old roots do fairly well the second year, young plants, raised from seeds or cuttings, are preferable. Violas, although often planted out in the spring, as a rule make a finer show when placed in their flowering quarters in the autumn.

Gaillardias also are still masses of gorgeous blossom. Very pretty they look where stake and string have been dispensed with, for the flower-crowned stalks, drooping to the ground, have a charmingly natural appearance.

As there are three primary colours, so there are three main principles or laws in colour combination. These are those of contrast, analogy and gradation.

CONTRAST

Taking the law of contrast first, let us see how it applies to our gardens. Take, for example, groups or clumps of sweet peas, which are in such favour to-day. Suppose a row of these clumps with each colour planted separately. It may not seem to matter how they succeed one another, but a knowledge of the law of contrast will show that much depends upon the relation of the colours to each other. Suppose the first clump to be one of the fine self-crimsons, then obviously it should not be succeeded by any of the purple or orange or lavender sorts, if the full value of the separate colours be desired; but it may be followed by any good yellow variety, as, after green, yellow is nearest being complementary to crimson, blue being a good second.

This, then, is the guiding principle in contrast, to find and supply the complementary of the colour in question. The complementary of a colour must contain just what the colour itself lacks of the three primaries. Instance, red and blue give purple; yellow is the complementary. Red and yellow give orange; blue is the complementary. Blue and yellow give green; red is the complementary.

KELWAY'S "ARTISTIC" BORDERS

Kelway Double Borders. Tracts of colour spreading right and left. All Kelway Borders can be so planned.

HERBACEOUS BORDER.

ANALOGY

The second of the laws of colour is that of analogy. It is rather more difficult than that of contrast, but is as helpful and necessary to the student of colour in the garden. The law of analogy deals with colours which are friendly and related, and which, when placed together mutually improve and strengthen each other. A fine example of analogy may be seen in the veining of a leaf, the proximity of trees and plants, which, though distinct in species and form, yet show a pleasing combination together, giving the light and shade which are so necessary to artistic work.

No hard and fast rule can be laid down here, as only experiment can determine the best combinations on analogous methods. One fine example I have seen was that of a small rhododendron bush with a full pink bloom surrounded by deep crimson wallflower. It was a most pleasing spring combination.

A BORDER *of* WHITE FLOWERS

To find a bed of white flowers in a garden is not as usual as it used to be. A border of white flowers is very rare, however, although it can be made exceedingly lovely. Of course, it may be in the open, by gravel paths or lawns, but its best effect is when it is backed by a red-brick wall.

Against a red-brick house is a delightful spot for this border. It should be so massed as to be floriferous at the three seasons, spring, summer and autumn ; while helleborus, snowdrops, and white hepaticas can be visible during winter.

The spring flowers will include white daphne, narcissi in quantity, tulips, hyacinths, crocuses, arabises, aquilegias, honesty, violas, pansies—all white varieties. Pinks, white pæonies, antirrhinums will be a little later.

The wonderful beauty of white begonias, marguerites, scabious, pelargoniums of all sections, dahlias, cosmeas, cornflowers, godetias, schizanthus, sweet peas, sweet sultans, stocks, asters, and poppies, large and small, is known to us all, but perhaps we cannot realise it fully until we see them apart from gay varieties.

Then there are white lupins, tall and dwarf, with ex-

KELWAY'S "ARTISTIC" BORDERS

No. 2. Kelway Spring Flowering Border. Price as for No. 1 "A" and No. 1 "B."

IN MY GARDEN
THIS MORNING

OCTOBER 8. The sunflowers and golden rods are now over, but Japanese anemones, rudbeckias, clematises, bravely put forth their last blossoms. Perfect flowers are still found on dahlias, gaillardias, penstemons, while a few gladioli are to-day fighting their way into the flowering line.

But the chief joys of the garden are the wonderful chrysanthemums and Michaelmas daisies. Where a feature has been made of the former plants (a large bed planted thickly with them) a lovely mass of colour delights one.

The later Michaelmas daisies (in shades of mauve, pink and white) gleam, studded with innumerable starry flowers, above the faded treasures of summer.

A SHELTERED CORNER FOR FAVOURITES.

quisite foliage, petunias, poppy anemones, irises, carnations, and campanulas, Agrostemma coelia-alba, sweet alyssum, Saponaria calabrica alba, Whitlavia grandiflora alba, candytufts, nemophila, lobelia, dianthus, Phlox Drummondi, Gilia nivalis, Jacobæa (seed of white only can be bought), Kaulfussia ammelliodes alba, Lavatera trimmestis alba, Leptosiphon densiflorus albus, Linaria bipartita, Malope grandiflora alba, Mesembryanthemum album, Myosotis alpestris and azorica alba, Nemesis floribunda alba, nicotianas, Nigella hispanica alba, Oenothere taraxacifolia alba, Polygonum alba, Sweet Williams, can be patronised.

A speciality might well be made of white verbenas, truly exquisite flowers for cutting and scent-yielding, also for white balsams, on account of their garden appearance. Two useful ground coverers are white Virginian stock, and Ver-

onica syriaca alba for spring effect. White zinnias are effective, and may be still in blossom with the chrysanthemums of autumn, as well as with the indispensable forms of Chrysanthemum maximum. Pyrethrum uliginosum and white Michaelmas daisies will be kept company by the geraniums, verbenas, petunias, etc., until sharp frosts come.

The white border is one that can be enriched by degrees ; gladioli, liliums, etc., can be introduced at appropriate times. Herbaceous beauties, such as hollyhocks or penstemons, may be added ; but in early summer all gaps can be filled with hardy and half-hardy annuals. *Amateur Gardening.*

FAMOUS NURSERIES

From *Land & Water.*

There are few gardeners who do not know the name of Kelway & Son, and who have not at some time or other grown plants sent out from the world-famous nurseries situated on the outskirts of Langport. It would be very hard to estimate the debt owed by the horticultural world to the two energetic partners of this most noteworthy firm, or to appreciate fully the untiring zeal of Mr. William and Mr. James Kelway in matters of horticultural enterprise.

It is a known fact that few people realise how important a part is played by a large firm in the welfare of the count-

IN MY GARDEN THIS MORNING

OCTOBER 18. A great frost has visited the garden. Yesterday morning ponds were covered with ice ; lawns and meadows, in the early sunshine, lay before one sparkling and white. Many flowers died in the night ; dahlias, so lately laden with beautiful blooms, now stand black and bowed. Even a few of the sturdy chrysanthemums are injured.

Yet several geraniums came safely through the wintry hours, proving that they are hardier subjects than is generally supposed.

To-day we walk in the garden beneath a blue sky, thinking of spring, more than content with the violets and primroses we have found in the wood.

KELWAY'S "ARTISTIC" BORDERS

No. 3. Kelway Summer Flowering Border. Price as for No. 1 "A" and No. 1 "B."

HERBACEOUS BORDER.

less gardens that exist both at home and abroad. The raising of new plants, the propagation of new varieties at great cost, and oft-times considerable loss owing to the fickleness of the gardening public, the recognised source of supply for innumerable specialities that from time to time are in demand, form some of the numberless features that make the existence of a nursery indispensable.

Great businesses do not come into being of their own accord, and where such exist it is very natural to ask who is the founder of the brains of the undertaking ; and one also likes to learn something of the rise of the business and its methods. We Englishmen have much to be proud of in our world-famed nurseries, and a great tribute of praise and respect is due to the heads of those firms that have done so much to make our land noted for its flowers and for its gardens. For half a century Messrs. Kelway have done more than any other firm to educate and supply the herbaceous gardener with the most up-to-date information, together with the very latest introduction in plants, and the numberless new varieties which bear their name are sufficient proof alone of the successes of this firm.

Their first great speciality was the Gladiolus, for which they soon became famous, and to-day, although many firms have specialised in this flower, they are still to the fore, devoting no less than twenty-five acres to Gladioli alone. Fifty years' experience has enabled them to place before

the public the most wonderful collections of these choice flowers, and their bulbs of this species are the finest that can be procured ; being well matured and of good size they produce large spikes of magnificent blooms such as are easily one of the greatest features of the herbaceous border.

But if I had to name Messrs. Kelway's greatest triumph I should unhesitatingly attribute it to their new herbaceous Pæonies, and I would like to predict for this most hardy and attractive flower a great future. Without doubt gardeners are beginning to realise its possibilities, and every year sees the introduction of new varieties. This, of course, will mean that very shortly many will specialise in the culture of this flower, and that classes will be devoted to it at our shows. And then the general public will become alive as to its real value. No herbaceous border can ever

KELWAY'S "ARTISTIC" BORDERS

No. 4. Kelway Autumn Border. Price as for No. 1 "A" and No. 1 "B."

IN MY GARDEN THIS MORNING

OCTOBER 29. In planning a garden we must try to avoid giving it a too formal appearance. For instance, do not place all the tall perennials at the back of a long border, but bring a few stately subjects close to the grass or gravel edge ; let the low-growing violas, rock cresses, etc., sometimes run up from the margin of the bed, to form rivers of colour among the sunflowers and phloxes.

Hyacinth and tulip beds must be more or less formally laid out, and will contrast well with wilder portions of the garden.

PICTURESQUE GROUPING OF HERBACEOUS PLANTS, FERNS AND SHRUBS IN SHADY WATERSIDE CORNER.

not only marked by fresh combinations of colour and larger petals for each flower, but without doubt the plants are finer, and I venture to think, more free flowering. As in the case of the Pæony so with the Delphinium, no herbaceous border is complete without it, and its height and charming variety of colour makes it an indispensable flower for any garden.

Yet one more speciality I would mention of the many for which Messrs. Kelway are famous, and this is the Pyrethrum, so popular with all gardeners. Their new varieties are too numerous to mention, and they testify to their careful selection and hybridisation. Easy of cultivation, this flower has also found special favour by reason of its exquisite grace and its invaluable use for cutting for indoor decoration. A new and enlarged list of varieties has added considerably to its demand and made it a flower universally sought after by small and large growers alike.

As to be expected, numerous and valuable awards have been won by Messrs. Kelway for all their notable introductions ; and it is seldom that an exhibit from their famous nurseries at Langport fails to secure the highest honours.

Nearly every herbaceous plant that is in commerce can be obtained from this firm, and their manual contains a most complete list of such, together with the finest seed and bulb list that can be desired. There is not a more artistic, more attractive, better illustrated, or better compiled catalogue in the whole of the British Isles, and in all probability in the world, than that which is known as **Kelway's "Manual of Horticulture."** It is, indeed, a thoroughly reliable and valuable work, and every floriculturist who has a large garden should try to secure a copy. In it he will find not only one of the most beautiful collections of illus-

afford to do without a choice collection of this wonderful flower, and no rough bank and waste piece of land can be more effectively planted up than when filled with this hardy, fine-foliaged, free-blooming plant.

When Messrs. Kelway first started to take in hand the Pæony, there were but a few varieties, yet now this firm, by years of careful hybridisation and selection, have given us literally hundreds of the most attractive sorts. Sweetly scented, and ever a mass of colour, the Pæony is bound to be always a popular flower, and it is necessary only to convince the public of its hardy nature and to dazzle their eyes at many shows with countless varieties to create quite a boom in this most ancient flower.

So many herbaceous plants have been improved by Messrs. Kelway, and so many owe their largely increased number of varieties to the efforts of this firm, that it is a very difficult matter to know which next to choose as being worthy of special mention, but I do not think we shall be far wrong if we select the Delphinium as being certainly one of their most valued specialities. Their new varieties are

IN MY GARDEN
THIS MORNING

NOVEMBER 8. The rain is over. Delightful it is to wander through the morning garden again, watching the steamy mist slowly roll away, and greeting at last a blue November sky.

How still a windless November day is—the distant caw of the rooks, the robin's occasional note, the patter of falling acorns, are the only sounds to be heard.

To-day but few blossoms can be found in the garden. Yet, as if to remind us that flower-time is only just over, a tall spike of white lupins rises from a bare, flat border, an over-brave tritoma flings high a ruddy torch.

A MICHAELMAS DAISY GARDEN.

KELWAY'S "ARTISTIC" BORDERS

No. 24. Kelway Hardy Bulb Border. Price on application.

trations of herbaceous flowers, but also a full description of each plant, together with such notes as the height to which they attain, the times of the year for their planting, etc. The book is a masterpiece in general compilation and sets a standard which might with advantage be emulated. No library in any private house that devotes a shelf to gardening literature should be without it, for it will ever remain one of the best works of reference in connection with the culture of herbaceous plants that the floriculturist can wish for.

There is also a supplement to Messrs. Kelway's **" Manual of Horticulture "** called "Gardens of Delight," a very attractive work that is illustrated with photographs and coloured plates of beautiful garden views that owe their glory and wealth of bloom to plants procured from the famous Langport nurseries. Such works depict very clearly the successes that can be achieved in any garden, and not only do they stimulate fresh endeavours and fire one with new ideas, but they furnish as well an invaluable guide in all our garden undertakings.

Since then the successes of our own gardens depend so largely upon the successes of the nursery from which we purchase our plants, we will, by congratulating Messrs. William and James Kelway on their past achievements, exclaim with all true gardeners at all seasons of the year, "Long may the nurseries of Langport flourish."

T. GEOFFREY W. HENSLOW, M.A.

A WELL-FILLED DOUBLE BORDER OF HERBACEOUS PERENNIALS.
With a semi-formal edging of violas.

COLOUR EFFECTS IN GARDEN AND BORDERS

HARMONY RATHER THAN CONTRAST.—Splendid harmonies of rich and brilliant colour, and proper sequences of such harmonies, should be the rule ; there should be large effects, each well studied and well placed, varying in different portions of the garden scheme.

BREADTH OF MASS AND INTERGROUPING.— It is important to notice that the mass of each colour should be large enough to have a certain dignity, but never so large as to be wearisome. A certain breadth in the masses is also wanted to counteract the effect of foreshortening when the border is seen from end to end. When a definite plan of colour is decided upon, it will save trouble if the plants whose flowers are approximately the same in colour are

A KELWAY PÆONY BORDER NEAR FARNHAM.

IN MY GARDEN
THIS MORNING

NOVEMBER 19. Though many hardy plants will flourish in almost any situation, there is generally an aspect in which they flower best.

We must always be trying to master the likes and dislikes of our plants. Thus, although primroses and bluebells will bloom nearly everywhere, they never increase so rapidly as when growing in a shady spot. Pæonies enjoy a west aspect, since the early morning sun is apt to harm the half-frozen buds.

Again, phloxes, hollyhocks, and most of the lilies, require a moist soil, while wallflowers, rock-roses, and snapdragons, need light and well-drained ground.

The Kelway Seat for Kelway Gardens

Deal, £2 5s.   Oak, £3 10s.   Teak, £3 17s. 6d.   See illustration, page 51.

A SMALL KELWAY HERBACEOUS BORDER IN JULY.
Greater width would have rendered it more effective, and the nearness
of the hedge is likely in time to prove a drawback.

eye unpleasantly. It will generally be found that one mass or group of white will be enough in any piece of border or garden arrangement that can be seen from any point of view.

BLUE requires rather special treatment, and is best approached by delicate contrasts of warm whites and pale yellows, such as the colours of the Double Meadow Sweet, and Œnothera Lamarckiana, but rather avoiding the direct opposition of strong blue and full yellow. Blue flowers are also very beautiful when completely isolated and seen alone among rich dark foliage.

A PROGRESSION OF COLOUR in a mixed border might begin with strong blues, light and dark, grouped with white and pale yellow passing on to pink; then to rose colour, crimson, and the strongest scarlet, leading to orange and bright yellow. A paler yellow followed by white would distantly connect the warm colours with the lilacs and purples, and a colder white would combine them pleasantly with low-growing plants with cool-coloured leaves.

SILVERY-LEAVED PLANTS are valuable as edgings and carpets to purple flowers, and bear the same kind of relation to them as the warm-coloured foliage of some plants do to their strong red flowers, as in the case of the Cardinal Flower and the double crimson Sweet William.—G. J. (MISS JEKYLL), in *The English Flower Garden*.

grouped together to follow each other in season of blooming. Thus, in a part of the border assigned to red, Oriental Poppies might be planted among or next to Tritomas, with a scarlet Gladioli between both, so that there should be a succession of scarlet flowers, the places occupied by the Gladioli being filled previously with red Wallflowers.

WARM COLOURS are not difficult to place; scarlet, crimson, pink, orange, yellow, and warm white are easily arranged so as to pass agreeably from one to the other.

PURPLE AND LILAC group well together, but are best kept well away from red and pink. They do well with the colder whites, and are seen at their best when surrounded and carpeted with grey-white foliage, like that of Cerastium or Cineraria maritima; but if it be desired to pass from a group of warm colour to purple and lilac, a good breadth of pale yellow or warm white may be interposed.

WHITE FLOWERS.—Care must be taken in placing very cold white flowers such as Iberis correæfolia, which are best used as quite a high light, led up to by whites of a softer character. Frequent repetitions of white patches catch the

A KELWAY DELPHINIUM WALK IN SURREY.
Charming in the extreme.

IN MY GARDEN
THIS MORNING

NOVEMBER 29. Stormy weather has returned, and outdoor work is again impossible. Yet round the fire there are fascinating catalogues to study, plans to make for next year's garden.

Few flowers are more charming than the anemones. Besides the popular coronaria species, there are the lovely wood anemones, which grow freely in shady beds.

Anemone blanda lights up a border with blue and white stars, while the apennina variety (easy to grow) is well worth cultivating.

The Kelway Pæony Seat for Pæony Borders

Deal, £2 10s. Oak, £3 17s. 6d. Teak, £4 5s. For illustration, see p. 51.

COLOUR IN THE GARDEN

THE MIDSUMMER PAUSE.—About the present time of year—a little earlier or later, according to the season—there comes a sort of solstice in the flower gardener's calendar, a pause which marks the high tide of his annual display. The evenings have not yet begun to draw in to any serious extent ; all the works for this season's adornment are finished, and those concerned with next year's are well in hand ; the borders have their full complement of beauty ; the gaps left by the spring blooms are grown over, the annuals have reached the flowering stage ; now, if ever, the general effect must justify or accuse the gardener. In the space of comparative leisure which comes at this period, it is almost an instinctive proceeding to review the main result, count the successes and failures, and settle the alterations of details or plan to be carried out before another year. There are few who in such a review are not conscious of room for considerable reforms. The gardener's art, whether, as some would say, it leads its followers naturally on from one perfection to another ; or whether, as others might put it, it inspires a restless spirit of change for change's sake, is certainly not a stationary influence : and if the gardener should chance to be constitutionally attached to the old ways, there is the external weight of fashion and the stress of public taste making itself felt and ultimately leading to innovation in all but the most rigidly conservative of borders.

Seventy years ago the bedding-out system began to break in upon the landscape and the formal styles ; in turn the

A RICH EFFECT FROM THE USE OF HERBACEOUS PLANTS INSTEAD OF "BEDDING" OR "FOLIAGE" PLANTS IN RATHER FORMAL SURROUNDINGS.

great herbaceous theory made good its ground, and closed the reign of the universal geranium. And now, though the flower-gardener is still bidden to devote himself chiefly to perennials, he begins to be conscious of new devices in his chosen field, and recognises, either as a zealous convert or an uncomfortable doubter, refinements upon the "mixed border" which not long ago was the height of taste—the virtues of "mass," that is to say, as contrasted with distribution, and the replacing of a gay variety by "unity and breadth." The ordinary amateur, who learned most of his art from the epoch-marking canons of "The English Flower Garden," suffers a painful shock when he hears his lavish beds, with their mixture of opulent colour, crudely called a muddle, and compared to a kaleidoscope or a crazy-quilt. He may at first defy the new learning : but the consciousness of being a little behind the fashion is a subtle influence, and the weight of important names, the talk of more advanced neighbours, and the study of books with colour-process illustrations begin before long to have their effect, till some autumn sees the sweeping alterations in the familiar ground, which are to get rid for ever of "spottiness"

THE PAVED GARDEN
A corner, hard in itself, rendered delightful with the informal use of suitable hardy plants.

Kelway Semi-Circular Border Seat

Design A. Deal, £7 10s. Oak, £11. Teak, £12 5s. For illustration, see page 51.

IN MY GARDEN
THIS MORNING

DECEMBER 10. The weather has become very mild. Buds can be seen on snowdrops growing in old-established clumps. One has only to remove a little soil to uncover the white shoots of crocuses and daffodils.

Plants which already show next year's flower-buds are of great interest now. Rhododendrons and azaleas are crowned with hundreds of them, while the barberries promise to light the garden with yellow and orange fires when spring comes. And one can tell where the white flowers of the mountain clematis will peep forth, where the lovely lilac blossoms will shoot up into the May sunshine.

A PLEACHED WALK.
With grass and flower borders; much to be desired, cool and quiet

comparatively little trouble by merely excluding actual jars of colour, chiefly to be found in the contact of the rawer scarlets with the duller crimsons, and of particular shades of purple and blue. On the positive side, the observer may learn how many families of flowers may be trusted to mingle their twenty different hues in perfectly happy domestic harmony. The aquilegias, carnations, Canterbury bells, pæonies, afford instances of delightful "mixtures," suave or sparkling, by the side of which the seclusion of "separate colours" would be at best a flat respectability. Another easy expedient lies in the sparing and judicious use of contrast—(how many gardeners who use the word remember that it means a fight?) A range of delphiniums, their spikes somewhat isolated by the green of their foliage, may, for all their differences of tone, easily present an aspect of rather heavy monotony : a single group of the buff Lilium testaceum in the right place, with a broad clump of the orange L. croceum below it, will make the spires above them kindle into sapphire flame. *The Times.*

and "restlessness" and to inaugurate the reign of mass, harmony and repose. During the first summer after the change there are various inevitable allowances to be made. Many things are checked and stunted by the shift ; there are gaps due to chances of the weather, or to oversight in planting ; and there are discords produced by lapses of memory or mixing the labels. All that will come right the year after. But unless the gardener possess unusual powers of management and artistic taste, it is probable that the second season will again fail entirely to content him. Perhaps, too, the critical sense has grown acuter ; not only in his own quarters, but in those of his fellow progressives, he finds grave lapses from the elevated standard. If he is a wise man, he will in the time between the full tide of the year and the season of dismantling and reform put back the whole question for further consideration.

He will probably learn from his experiments two or three points of experience which may be very useful in the conduct of the herbaceous border of the older kind. One of these, on the negative side, is that a good deal may be done with

BEAUTY AND ECONOMY ALLIED

" Everyone interested in the trend of modern horticulture must have been gratified with the decided swing of the pendulum of late years in favour of the old English Border, which, for the time, had to give way to the passing craze for gaudier colouring that dazzled rather than delighted the eye, and was never in the least likely to satisfy the artistic sense.

AN INFORMAL MIXED BORDER IN ESSEX.

IN MY GARDEN THIS MORNING

DECEMBER 20. The campanulas (bell-flowers), are some of the grandest of our hardy garden plants, and are all easily grown. A collection of them is very fascinating. The tall campanulas include glomerata (deep violet in clusters), latifolia (enormous drooping bells of satiny lilac, purple, or white flowers), persiæfolia (one of the finest sections, including many popular garden varieties).

The charming "Canterbury Bells" and the wonderful "Chimney Bell-flower" are biennials, and must be renewed yearly.

Kelway Quadrant Border Seat

Design B. Deal, £8. Oak, £11 15s. Teak, £13 5s. Illustrated on page 51.

Colour scheme in the garden we *must* have, in which the border plays an important part ; but how few there are who can carry out even to their own satisfaction the least ambitious of such schemes ! Then what mistakes are made year after year in the arrangement of garden borders ! The rapid spreading of some plants is not allowed for here, the tall growth of others is unforeseen there ; in short, the borders are frequently but ludicrous failures where the over-confident amateur has given himself too free a hand. The question of border arrangement is full of detail. Perfection is not to be attained without the expenditure of much time and a considerable amount of skill and patience.

"Simplicity, together with taste, for which we all strive, is after all attained only by the few ; and yet the amateur has no real cause to despair. More and more has expert attention been paid to this subject of garden borders in recent years, and Mr. James Kelway, of Langport, Somerset, in his firm's excellent 'Manual of Horticulture,' points the way to certain success. It is next to impossible to explain in cold print how to plant an herbaceous border ; but with the carefully worked-out schemes before one, the mind is clearly impressed, and one grasps the fact that it is not only possible to have a beautiful border in one's garden in spring and summer and autumn, but a border that will throughout conform to the highest canon of artistic taste.

"Messrs Kelway & Son's borders, it may be well to point out, are chiefly composed of hardy perennials arranged according to the season of their bloom, and perhaps they have done more to increase the enjoyment of gardening and decrease the cost than any other horticultural development

BOLDLY MASSED PERENNIALS—A WEALTH OF FLOWERS.

of recent years. The 'Kelway Garden' is, indeed, the garden that may be said to approach the ideal." *County Gentleman.*

PERENNIAL PLEASURES

"'One ray of sunshine to five hundred and sixty-seven thousand gallons of water' is a foreigner's summary of our climate. That seems an accurate estimate when one considers the disastrous end of many a pretty garden. I wonder how many thousands of tender 'bedding' plants were discouraged by cold and wet in 1903 ! One dreadful suburban enclosure that I knew in June was planted so thickly—some-one had given *carte blanche*—with red geraniums, blue lobelias, yellow calceolarias, *and* magenta petunias, that the *tout* was like a bad dream. But July floods and August storms and September tornadoes wrecked the place so thoroughly that the colours have long been washed out.

KELWAY'S DELPHINIUMS IN THE BORDER.

Kelway Trellis for Border Backgrounds

Per lineal yard—Deal, 8s. 6d. Oak, 10s. See illustration, page 51.

IN MY GARDEN
THIS MORNING

DECEMBER 31. Looking forward, our thoughts are all of next year's garden. "Next year's garden" should always be more beautiful than "last year's garden." The gardener, if he loves his flowers, gains knowledge every day, and besides continually improving his plot of ground, should grow new flower-treasures each year. Spring, summer, and autumn will then never lose their precious charms.

A KELWAY GARDEN IN YORKSHIRE.

hear nightingales singing of delicious misery—and, being thus wrought upon, they order numberless roots to be sent across the water. Now that there is a parcel-post service, it is a simple thing to get them over, and the fleshy roots travel perfectly. It would astonish an English gardener, indeed, to see the profusion of Kelway Pæonies in American gardens, but they grow quite as well in our chilly mists.

"And as for Delphiniums, I never had better ones than this year's. They had good drainage and what little sunlight there was, and they made the most of these advantages. The white 'Beauty of Langport' thrusting up its fine spikes among a quantity of white Lilies was very beautiful, but the blue beds were the joy of the garden—sapphire, turquoise, amethyst. They were glorious in the sun, and there was a curious metallic one that might have been almost anything but a flower—say, a huddle of humming-birds. Positively the glittering things emitted a knowing irridescent wink as one went by. . . .

"Let us profit by the American cousin, and get all these good things *in time*. The sooner they are planted in our gardens the sooner they will be making growth. They—and dozens of other Perennials of Kelway's raising—are tough and hardy as anything that grows. If the ten bad summers come true, if they swamp out all our dainty plants bred under glass, still Kelway's hybrid beauties will keep us in blossoms of the highest types of loveliness—of noblest forms and most exquisite colours. Most of our pleasures are expensive, but it is not so with these Perennials, which are practically an investment, for they grow and increase with the years, and the modest outlay at first repays itself again and again in the gorgeous results." *The Onlooker*.

It has been a bad time for 'bedding' plants—for all the things that we buy such acres of glass, such miles of hot-water pipes, to rear—but it has been a wonderful triumph for the Messrs. Kelway of Langport, Somerset.

"Everyone who has gardened knows that the cult of the hardy perennial owes its being to the Kelways; no other grower has produced such superb new varieties of things that were absolutely hardy to start with. The Pæony, for example—and 'pæony' is almost a synonym for 'Kelway'—asks for nothing in the way of climate; only put it in good earth and its buds will unfold in the teeth of a driving north-east gale; the rigours of our spring are nothing to it. Even when other hardy flowers were torn to pieces I saw pæonies blooming magnificently in a dozen gardens that I know during the late—alleged—summer. Many a pilgrimage to Langport is made by visiting Americans; they go to see the latest creations evolved by the genius of the place—the marvels of burnished gold stamens and silken petals in countless variations of cream and rose hues; they give themselves up to the witchery of pæony perfume, and, closing their eyes, see moonlight and dark red Roses, and

BORDER OF KELWAY'S PÆONIES, NEAR NEWBURY, BERKS.

IN MY GARDEN THIS MORNING

JANUARY 10. The days are appreciably longer now, and since the weather remains mild, plant-growth begins to move again. Even the larkspurs, day lilies, the early monkshood, lupins, appear above ground. Many roses are making growth.

What a charming bunch of flowers one can pick up on a mild January day! Snowdrops, winter aconites, wallflowers, a few violets, winter sweet, yellow jessamine, primroses, coloured cowslips, polyanthus, Christmas roses! And then there are always many stray blossoms of summer and autumn plants which each year surprise us by opening in the so-called dull and uninteresting gardening months.

PERGOLA CHAIN

3s. 9d. per dozen yards.

The Daily Mail (1907) quotes Kelway & Son when it says :—

"Ladies and gentlemen rarely leave things completely to their paid gardener now as they did years ago. They now bring their own refinement and taste to bear, and the result has been that a marvellous progress has been effected from an artistic and scientific point of view.

"We now see no more of the flat carpet-bed with its trim conventionalities. The ideal of 'flowers all the year round' is now being very nearly realised in the herbaceous borders of our gardens."

❦

And *The Daily Telegraph* has awakened to the value of the Artistic Borders advocated by Kelway & Son :—

"THE CARPET GARDENER.—Nor have we to congratulate ourselves alone on the wealth of lovely things rewarding the zeal of the modern horticulturist, and those who collect for him. The bad old times of the carpet bedder and the gardener whose art was inspired by the wall-paper man were doomed to give way to a better understanding of flowers and a higher appreciation of their real beauty, and to-day the formal and artificial have been all but banished from our midst.

"It was William Morris who once refused to speak of the Carpet Gardener, confessing he blushed with shame even to think of him."

❦

A PERENNIAL BORDER.
Adding to the beauty of one of the "stately homes of England." Far finer than the old ribbon parterre.

The ARCHITECTURAL GARDEN

"As we have often insisted in these columns, the architectural 'setting' of a house is to a great extent determined in effectiveness by the treatment of its surroundings, whether an open space or courtyard in a city or a garden in country or suburbs. In modern times the up-to-date landscape gardener has for nearly a century past succeeded in killing all attempts at gardening as an adjunct to architecture. 'Bedding out,' winding walks, meaningless clumps of shrubs, and tortuous changing of natural contour and level into something totally different, have completed the divorce of the arts of architecture and garden craft or design. In England the fancy for the old and characteristic formal garden is becoming every day more widely prevalent, and we hope that soon in Ireland people, and in particular architects, may hasten the return of the lost art. Characteristic of old-fashioned and architectural gardens, with

A KELWAY TOWN GARDEN.
Showing what can be done with good perennials in gardens of modest dimensions.

The Kelway Label in Steel for Herbaceous Plants

4/- per dozen. 30/- per 100. See page 52.

IN MY GARDEN
THIS MORNING

JANUARY 14. Flowers, trees, verdant lawns, pretty walks, beautiful climbers, these are the chief joys of a garden.

Now is a good time to put up arches or a pergola—*i.e.*, a colonnade of arches. Roses, clematis, vines, jessamines, honeysuckles, etc., can be planted to grow over them. What more charming picture has a garden than a well-covered pergola, or arches draped with lovely climbers ?

Climbers, too, should be trained over the house. Even the humblest villa can, in a few years, be made to look attractive. A bare wall should not be tolerated.

their charming combinations of flowers, turf, fruit, and water, was the herbaceous border—most beautiful of features in these hard northern climes, affording almost an all-the-year-round display of colour in rich and gay old-fashioned, sweet-scented flowers, that were known and loved long before even the modern delicate bedding-out plant, or even Dutch bulb, became popular in England or Ireland.

" We have lately seen a manual and catalogue of Messrs. Kelway & Son, of the Royal Seed and Plant Establishment, Langport, Somerset. This firm make a speciality of old-fashioned herbaceous plants notable for colour, sweet scent, and hardiness, particularly adaptable to **architectural** gardening. Architects desirous of seeing the surroundings of houses designed by them converted into a suitable setting might do much worse than consult Messrs. Kelway."

The Irish Builder and Engineer.

"A GARDEN OF HARDY FLOWERS.—A wonderful change has been wrought during the last five years in the floral decorations of British gardens. The florid, strictly geometrical, and stereotyped fashion of planting flower beds with wonderful mosaic patterns, and borders with line after line of gaudy, tender exotics, graduated with almost mathematical exactness from back to front, has happily given way to a more sensible, beautiful, and appropriate style of garden decoration. Owners of gardens are beginning to realise that there is a hundredfold more pleasure, beauty, and attractiveness to be obtained by the judicious selection and tasteful disposition of hardy plants of a permanent character than there is in the old system of filling the garden with tender plants whose beauty and attractiveness are of an ephemeral and doubtful nature.

THE OLD IDEA

" Twenty years ago a border would have been tabooed by the majority of garden owners as a weedy thing unworthy of a moment's appreciation. It would have been planted with a row of double show or fancy Dahlias at the back, followed in order of height by Amaranthus, Marigold, Geraniums, Irises, Calceolarias, Petunias, Lobelias, and Feverfew. Such a border would reach its attractive stage by about August, and by the middle of September begin to gradually lose its beauty, if beauty be the correct term to use in such a case. In autumn, bulbs, Wallflowers, Forget-me-not, Daisies, and Primroses would be planted to blossom in the springtime. Here, also, the same rule as to graduation of height would be observed, and the result may well be imagined. This sort of gardening found favour mainly because owners rarely bothered themselves about what was planted in the garden so long as a brilliant show of colour was obtained. They were content to pay heavy bills for fuel to maintain the necessary heat to propagate and grow the myriads of tender plants that were needed, or to pay the

local nurseryman large sums where the supply had to be purchased. The average professional gardener in those days prided himself more on the splendid collection of bedding plants that he reared from seed or cuttings, and on his geometrical ability in arranging them in the beds and borders, than on any other feature in the garden.

THE MODERN ONE

" But fashion has, thank heaven, changed since those days. Greenhouses are put to more legitimate and useful purposes, and the time of the gardener is more profitably employed. The beds are planted more prettily and artistically, and the borders converted into real objects of beauty where the garden is presided over by an owner with the true gardening instinct. What were formerly regarded as mere weedy subjects are now treasured and estimated at their proper value." *Amateur Gardening.*

" The best *centrepiece* for a garden is a water feature. The poorest is a bed of tender plants. Sundials are not strong enough for large gardens, but may be in little ones. A fountain or water-lily basin or pool is better.

" The best *borders* are deep ones—*e.g.*, 12 by 14 feet wide, and set off by vine-covered walls or hedges. It is impossible to get richness and massiveness in these poor, thin, little three-foot borders we see everywhere. The best arranged borders have only one large mass of each flower. Avoid repeating and dotting.

" The best *beds* are of simple shapes, not complicated ones. Fancy beds emphasise the smallness of a garden ; simple beds do not. Make all beds rectangular, except those which have to fit odd places. Avoid stars and crescents, and use circles only around circular features, such as pools or sundials.

" The best way to get *brilliancy* is by flowers ; the poorest is by gaudy foliage plants, like coleus. Have grass enough in the garden to rest the eyes occasionally from colour, and to make the flowers seem brighter by contrast.

" The best way to get a *succession of flowers* is not to take up bulbs every year and replace with bedding plants and annuals, for the expense of keeping tender plants over winter and starting annuals in hotbeds gets tiresome and suggests straining after effect. Have 90 per cent. of the plants permanent ; let only 10 per cent. or less be temporary. Shrubs, bulbs and creepers can be combined so as to give three or four crops of bloom in every bed.

" The best way to get *colour harmony* is to have a simple colour-scheme not a complicated one. The simplest plan is to avoid the one colour that makes nine-tenths of the colour discords—*viz.*, magenta and near magenta—anything which the catalogues call purple, crimson or mauve. The remaining discords are most easily softened by having plenty of green foliage and white flowers—the two peacemakers.

" The best *plants* are hardy plants, because they harmonise with the environment better than tender ones, are more permanent, and cost less to maintain. Nine times out of ten hardy plants will accomplish your purpose better than tender plants.

" The best way to get *year-round beauty* is not to make a list of your favourite flowers, but to make a list of the months, and provide about three main attractions (not necessarily flowers) for each month. For winter have broad-leaved evergreens, shrubs with brightly-coloured twigs, and berries that are attractive all winter, especially red berries. WILHELM MILLER.

IN MY GARDEN
THIS MORNING

JANUARY 25. It is a sure sign that spring has not come when amateur gardeners and others write to the newspapers proclaiming the birth of snowdrops, primroses, etc.

In reality, the early appearance of these flowers is not extraordinary, though it was interesting to read that monthly roses were picked last week in Devonshire.

It only shows that deep down in our hearts we are all waiting for the spring. Year after year it is the same. Though a garden-lover should live to be ninety, he will still eagerly watch for the first primrose, still be thrilled by the skylark's first song.

SANDSTONE ROCKERY STONE

4/- per ton, free on rails, at loading station.

"There can be no question that the firm of Kelway & Son, of Langport, Somerset, have been very largely instrumental in raising the herbaceous border from being a mere jumble of perennial favourites into a position of dignified and artistic worth unimagined hitherto, and their valuable work is now receiving well-deserved recognition. In the past year they have obtained for flowers of their own raising or introduction, grown at Langport, the following exhibition awards :—Five gold medals—*viz.*, Coronation Exhibition, London, Southampton Horticultural Society, Taunton Horticultural Society, Cardiff Horticultural Society and Royal Botanic Society, London ; four silver-gilt medals of the Royal Horticultural Society, London, and eight silver medals of the same society. Surely this constitutes a record for one year's awards."

Country Life.

THE JULY GARDEN. — With the Larkspurs (Delphiniums) comes the climax of the year in the garden. There may be a brighter show afterwards with half-hardy plants ; but the border of hardy perennials should now be at its best, with the purity of colour, stateliness of growth and profusion of bloom in which well-established hardy plants surpass all others. While it flowers the larkspur is king of the border, and those who wish to have their gardens splendid in July should plan them so that nothing may mar the larkspur's glory. This is as much as to say that blue should be the dominant colour of the July border, for the glory of the larkspur is in its blue. When it tries to be purple or mauve it has many rivals ; but none, or only one, when its spires shine as if with their own blue light. Sometimes a slight pink flush on pale blue larkspurs has a beautiful sunset effect, especially if the flowers have a dark eye ; and such flowers will look all blue at a distance. But the gardener will be wise to have his larkspurs as blue as possible, and to plan the whole border so that, at this time of year, it will harmonise with their blueness. He need not be timid in his scheme of colour. He may vary his blues through every shade from dark to light, and he may diversify them, not only with white, but with yellow and even with certain shades of pink. For without a bold diversity his border will look too calculated and will lack those surprises which are the glory of Oriental colour. We soon tire of colour harmonies unless here and there they astonish us by just escaping what we should expect to be certain discord. Only so do they have the strangeness that is necessary to all beauty and seems to have been achieved for the first time.

Therefore have a great variety of blues in your July border, provided not by larkspurs alone. For the larkspur has a new rival in the Dropmore variety of Anchusa italica, and a rival, luckily, who lives on excellent terms with him. The colours of the Anchusa and of all pure blue larkspurs go well together, and in form they set off each other ; for while the larkspur is simple and aspiring, the Anchusa spreads and bends its flowery branches, so that the two together are like Lombardy poplars with beeches. This comparison with trees comes naturally, for both plants in the border have a kind of forest grandeur ; and their blue, seen from across the garden, seems to have the enchantment of distance in it. The Anchusas, then, and the taller larkspurs should form the background, and some of the dwarfer syringas planted among them will make a beautiful contrast with their innumerable white stars. But besides the blue and white there should be a contrast of yellow ; and nothing gives this so well, among the taller plants, as Lilium testaceum, which from its height is also called Lilium excelsum. Its flowers are of a pale

apricot colour, and it has scarlet anthers. It is easy to grow, and in many gardens thrives better than the Madonna lily, especially if it is moved every three or four years, for it is a heavy feeder and soon exhausts the soil. In front of these taller plants may be placed Delphinium Belladonna, whose pale blue flowers look most brilliant against the darker blue of the Anchusa : and this may be mixed with Lilium hansoni, a fine Japanese lily that grows as well as the tiger lily in any good soil that is not too heavy, and in any position that is not too sun-baked. But it is never wise to speak certainly of lilies. Nearly all of them have their caprices : and because you have succeeded with them in one garden you must not assume that you will succeed in another which seems to offer just the same conditions. Lilium testaceum and Lilium hansoni are easy lilies, but some good gardeners fail with them, as they fail with the Madonna lily. The commonest cause of failure is lack of nourishment ; for all these lilies, at any rate in light soils, like as much food as they can get. They like manure, not only under their bulbs, but on the surface of the soil, and this should be given them just when they are passing out of flower. But it should not be forked in, for their roots are near the surface and hate to be disturbed. The Madonna lily, of course, should be in every July border. Indeed, it is, with the larkspur, the chief flower of July : and the best way to keep it free from disease is to plant it early, to feed it well year by year, and never to disturb it in any way. If it must be moved, dig it up as soon as it dies down.

So far our border is all blue and white, with the yellows of the two lilies, which should be kept well apart. But we have not yet considered the foreground, which must have its blues, too ; and where another colour may be introduced. The Belladonna larkspur is a pale blue for the middle, which looks beautiful against the darker blues behind it, and with the strong contrast of L. hansoni. For the foreground there is another larkspur which provides a yet paler blue, and that is the new variety of Delphinium grandiflorum, the colour of which is almost a French grey. It is only about 18 inches high, and can be easily raised from seed. Indeed, it is best to raise seedlings every two or three years, as old plants are apt to deteriorate or die out. It is of peculiar value in a blue border as a means of accomplishing the transition from the brighter blues of the background to a greater variety of colours in the foreground. It harmonises perfectly with all soft and pure pinks, and if it is mixed with them, it prevents them from seeming too little related to the mass of stronger blues behind. With it may be mixed either soft pink Sweet Williams, or some of the dwarf pink Polyantha roses, such as Gloire des Polyanthes or Aschenbrodel. The front of the border, among other low-growing flowers, is the place for these little Polyantha roses, and they should be treated as if they were herbaceous plants ; that is to say, cut back hard after their July flowering, in which case they will grow up again and flower well in about six weeks.

The Times.

IN MY GARDEN
THIS MORNING

FEBRUARY 2. The warmer weather of the past few days has wrought a change in the garden. Many plants peep above ground. Every mild morning will be interesting now. Some lupins, phloxes, Michaelmas daisies, have started to grow.

At this season it is interesting to compare the various ways that bulbs and tubers begin their growth.

The flower of the winter aconite coming straight out of the soil, the green foliage of the anemone rising two months before blossom-time. The beautiful habit of the snowdrop, scilla, blue-bell. The stately manner of the hyacinth, the awkward tulip.

YORKSHIRE STONE — BEST HARD

16/- per ton. See page 52.

A KELWAY BORDER.

Equal First Prize,
Kelway Photo Competition, 1913.

W. Jesper, Esq.

PHOTOGRAPHS OF KELWAY BORDERS

sent in by clients,
in December, 1913.

A KELWAY BORDER.

High Summer in the Garden.

W. Jesper, Esq.

"Portion of a KELWAY NO. 1 'A' ARTISTIC HERBACEOUS COLOUR BORDER. Planted in December, 1912. Photograph taken in late July, 1913, six months after planting, and showing Delphiniums, Michaelmas Daisies and Pæonies in full bloom. The Delphiniums continued in flower until late August. The garden is a suburban garden, in the midst of a large town, and formed the subject of an article in *Country Life* on December 13th, 1913. The 'raised herbaceous border' referred to in that article as having done marvellously and as having supplied bloom the whole of the year, is the border shown in this photograph."—E. A WALMISLEY. December 23rd, 1913.
Equal First Prize, Kelway Photo Competition, 1913.

SOME LETTERS

..*from*..

CLIENTS PLEASED WITH THEIR KELWAY BORDERS

✦

SEC. TO H.R.H. PRINCESS—
KENSINGTON PALACE, W.

"The new Herbaceous Border has done extremely well: much better than her Royal Highness anticipated."

✦

GERRARDS CROSS, BUCKS.

"I acknowledge with much pleasure and satisfaction receipt of the collection of plants for my border, together with plan for planting, and desire to express my admiration of the perfect condition in which the plants arrived, the quality of same, and last but by no means least, the courtesy and prompt attention given me."

✦

LONDON.

"I have never written to thank you for the splendid collection of flowers you recently sent me for a border in my front garden at Hampstead. I much appreciated the careful way in which the plants were labelled and packed."

✦

MIDLOTHIAN.

"You supplied me last year with a very fine selection of Border plants for an Artistic Herbaceous Border. This Border did very well last year and the planting in colour masses is most effective and beautiful. I should like to have the same kind of Border."

✦

PENSHURST,
KENT.

"The plants were beautifully packed, and I thought excellently fine specimens, and so did my gardener who was enthusiastic.

He says we shall have the best show in Penshurst.

Thanking you for your care in executing this order."

KELWAY'S "ARTISTIC" BORDERS

No. 6 "A." Kelway Pæony Border. 20/- per 10 square yards; with bulbs between, 40'- per 10 square yards.

IN MY GARDEN THIS MORNING

FEBRUARY 27. It is a great pity one so seldom sees single roses in gardens, for there are many beautiful varieties, easy to grow and very showy.

One of the best is Bellefleur, a truly lovely subject for hedges or pillars, having fiery crimson flowers with bright yellow anthers. Another splendid crimson is the carmine pillar.

Polyantha grandiflora (large white) is a very vigorous grower, and requires plenty of room; while the new Waltham rambler (rosy pink in clusters) should be in every garden. The single Austrian and Rugosa roses are very popular and useful.

TYWARDREATH.

" About 12 months ago you supplied me with the plants for a Small Border; and they have given the *greatest satisfaction.*"

❧

LONDONDERRY.

" I take this opportunity of saying how very pleased I am with the plants supplied by you for my Herbaceous Border. After being established about 2 years the plants have attained the most wonderful and gratifying growth. During the last few weeks the borders have been an object of admiration to all those who have seen them."

❧

NORTH SYDNEY, CANADA.

" The collection of plants arrived in wonderful order after their long journey, and the plan you sent proved invaluable.

I do not see how you can send so many lovely plants so cheaply.

With many thanks."

❧

BELMONT, SURREY.

" The borders that you arranged for us have done splendidly; the Lupines aud Delphiniums are still flowering well, and I really believe they have bloomed continually since April. The Delphiniums were so early. Also the Anchusa was really perfectly beautiful for a very long time."

❧

RAWAL PINDI,
PUNJAB, INDIA.

". . . . . I would like to continue dealing with you; your goods are most reliable and your packing is unequalled, which means that one can always depend on your plants, etc., arriving in good condition."

❧

HEATON, BOLTON.

" Received the plants on the 14th in good condition. Planted them as directed, and they have scarcely flagged at all, but I may say that they are all looking very well at present. I had some friends staying with me, and they all remarked on the excellent condition they were in.

I must thank you for your attention and plan; also the way in which the plants were packed."

❧

BRAMHALL, CHESHIRE.

" I have pleasure in writing to congratulate you on the way you have planned and arranged the Border, and to thank you for the fine selection of plants, which arrived in splendid condition."

**IN MY GARDEN
THIS MORNING**

MARCH 5. Several days of brilliant sunshine have brought out thousands of yellow crocuses. Dazzlingly beautiful they look edging along beds, or completely covering grass banks and patches of rough turf. Round them numberless bees gaily hum. Winter seems a season of the past.

Few people recognise the decorative value of large masses of crocuses in bloom in early March. Without them the garden would to-day be almost bare of flowers, instead of being paved with colour. Daffodil time has also begun. The first bud has burst. From now until November the garden will be a place of lovely flowers.

KELWAY'S "ARTISTIC" BORDERS

No. 7. Kelway Delphinium Border. £7 10s. 0d. per 100 plants; 10 square yards from 20/- upwards.

FROM A WELL-KNOWN ARCHITECT.

" I build houses from the £500 Cottage to Mansions for Millionaires in Park Lane. I always specify your Borders for the gardens."

FROM AN AMATEUR GARDENER.

" I am thinking of planting a few borders with perennials. I am tired of continually planting bedding plants."

GREENOCK.

" You will be pleased to hear that the £10 or so which I have sent you in the last few years has made my garden (¼ acre) one beautiful mass of colour all the year round. This year especially the place has been a perfect picture—quite as fine as any of the pictures in Walter Wright's 'Perfect Garden.' "

WENTWORTH, NEAR ROTHERHAM.

" The plants reached me safely, and we have got them all planted out. Your directions were so very clear and the packing so well done we found no difficulty whatever."

CUMBERLAND LODGE, WINDSOR.

" I have to thank you for your letter of the 1st inst., and have to say that their Royal Highnesses much appreciate your methods of doing business."

LA VILLE AU ROI, GUERNSEY.

" The plants I got from you in the beginning of May for my herbaceous border have done so marvellously well that even the Guernsey gardener can scarcely believe his eyes.

" I am sending you two photos, one of my border. As regards the border, planted about the middle of April, a friend of mine who is a great amateur gardener, saw it in August, and said that he would not have believed that it had only been planted four months. He thought that at least the plants had been there three years. I myself have never seen better plants sent out by any other firm."

GORTON, NEAR MANCHESTER.

" The goods, which you despatched on Thursday, arrived here safely on Saturday. After reading the numerous letters of thanks and congratulations which you have received from all quarters and classes, it almost seems like presumption on my part to attempt to say anything further, and yet I feel so grateful to you for your kind attention to my small order, and the courteous treatment which I have received from you, that I felt it requisite that I should express it in some way. The extreme care which has been taken in packing, labelling, etc., and the kindly help afforded me in the arrangement of my small garden, deserve and receive my warmest thanks. If there should be any way in which I can show it, either by recommendation or personal orders, you may be assured that I will do so."

KELWAY'S "ARTISTIC" BORDERS

No. 8. Kelway Lupine Border. Including all shades of soft yellows, lilacs, purples and blues. Price on application.

**IN MY GARDEN
THIS MORNING**

MARCH 11. Many beautiful varieties of the anemones can now be seen preparing to lay sheets of colour over the ground. Buds of the scarlet windflowers have arisen from the soil; another burst of sunshine will bring them out. These are natives of the south of France, and make a most brilliant show.

Anemone blauda (blue blossoms, from Greece) and appennina have also sent up their young green, while our native wood anemones, nestling round the roots of trees and encircling ferns in shady spots, to-day give welcome sign of their presence.

PICTURE GARDENS

SOME of the most delightful gardens are to be found in many villages in rural England. They are not confined to any particular county, or district. You find them in Cornwall and Devon; in Somerset and Gloucestershire; but you also come across them in East Anglia, in the hamlets about the Derbyshire dales, and in many parts of Yorkshire. One naturally asks what is the chief charm of these gardens that have about them so much to attract that compel one to pause and admire them? It is, I think, just this—they are full of beautiful old-time flowers, arranged not in any particular manner, or after some prescribed plan, but rather lacking in this, they have about them in their apparent want of order a loveliness that excites the admiration of all those who see them. These gardens are known to the readers of AMATEUR GARDENING.

You are perhaps on a holiday tour, and suddenly in a bend of the road you are brought face to face with a low-roofed dwelling, over-run with roses and clematises. Near the door-way, there is a porch festooned with sweet-scented jasmine; nay, before you see the house you are conscious of the delightful fragrance of the climber. Close to the hedge, maybe, is a group of hollyhocks, partly screening the house from view, but the garden gate is open, and as you stay to admire, not infrequently, the owner comes out and if it happens to be anywhere in Yorkshire or Lancashire it is almost certain that you will receive the "Coom in; dost tha' like flowers?" and if you love flowers, and you are wise, you will accept of the hearty invitation, and enter.

You will notice, as I have done, many a time, that of all the plants growing there, none appear to be more in evidence than the old-time flowering plants—brilliant pæonies, irises that cluster in borders near the doorway with bold splashings of colour on their petals, larkspurs that rise tall, sheer above most things in the garden, studies in blues and mauves and rosy-purples; dielytras with pink racemes that droop like miniature "blowbellows," so called by the children of the village. Campanulas, too, are everywhere to be seen—some tall, with bells of rich blue or purest white; others again in miniature, clustering about the rockery or, as is often the case, clinging amongst the rock cresses on the copings of the stone walls of the garden. There are pyrethrums, too, grown in these country gardens in all their delightful colourings, both double and single, and here and there gorgeous Oriental poppies that give a decided tone to the place. Foxgloves and penstemons also find a home here, and along the garden path, edged by rough stones, pansies and thrift, and not a few saxifragas are cultivated. Here are to be seen often things like lavender and sweet briar, honeysuckles and rosemary, mingling with the sweet-scented rockets that betray their presence at nightfall.

In a word, these gardens, typical of rural England, are the real picture gardens, the gardens that increase in beauty every year; that yield the very best investment for the outlay, because in nearly every case the initial expense is the only expense, as when once they have been planted one has but to divide the roots at stated periods, and so increase the attractiveness of the place. These picture gardens appeal to the artist, who loves to depict them on canvas. Their composition is such as to attract him because about them there is less of artificiality than is mostly seen in modern gardens, bound down, as they often are, by crude designs in beds that are spoken of as "ornamental."

And these picture gardens are not always confined to the country; they are not the monopoly of the dweller beyond the suburbs, for one may grow most of the old-time flowering plants with a good measure of success in the suburbs of many towns. It is often said that "hardy plants take a long time to grow to make anything like a show." There is no greater fallacy. You may plant this spring and have a reward this year if you take care to mulch the surface of the ground afterwards with rotted manure, and to plant in good loam or the best substitute for such. That is where so many people who love the old-fashioned flowers, but who do not grow them, make a mistake. They regard them as plants requiring establishing several years before their beauty is seen. A trial, however, will convince even the most sceptical that, even in a year from planting, one may have a garden where the borders from early summer, with the advent of the early irises, to the brilliant spikes of tritomas in September, or the flowers of the Michaelmas daisies, will prove a never-ending source of delight.

And these subjects go to rest, as is known, in the late autumn, appearing again in the spring, increasing in beauty each succeeding summer, justifying the statement that it is possible for many to have these picture gardens near their own homes—gardens that yield many blossoms that may be cut to brighten the home, and about which in the country one is often hearing the verdict from strangers, as they stop to admire, that verdict which carries with it clear conviction as to the value of the treasures of the garden, "How beautiful!"

W. LINDERS LEA.

Plants should be arranged in groups, not in ones or threes, as frequently done.
From a Client.

¶ "It appears to me to be quite impossible to lay down any fixed number of plants for all varieties. Some plants are large, some small; some spread and cover the ground, others do not; some when put in to fill a given area would be put in a matter of inches apart (small things), others feet apart. Therefore, even if the whole Border were divided into approximately equal spaces for all varieties, with one variety to each space (as in the last case), it seems to me that the number to put into the space would vary according to the variety from one to quite a large number.

¶ But again, some plants look best as individual specimens, some in clumps, others in masses or sheets of varying size, some repeated at intervals, etc., and I should have thought that this would have rendered it quite impossible, when designing a Border for good effect, to fix on any definite number of plants for all varieties alike. For instance—merely as an example—single Anchusas or Hyacinthus candicans may look very well among other things, but Delphiniums look best in large clumps, or better still in masses; while many things which are small and do not spread much look foolish as single plants, and require a good patch to be effective, in which case, they should be put in at the right distance apart to produce effect, perhaps 6in. or so, and a number would be required for the patch.

¶ A Border should be mapped out with varying areas for different varieties, as they look best, and the number of plants of each variety would then depend entirely on the *number and size of the areas* given to that variety, and *the distance apart it would be usual to put them in* to fill their *area or areas.*

¶ Of course, in borders like those under consideration there is not room for broad masses, but the *principle* can be equally well followed on a suitable scale, and the number of plants of each variety made to suit the space or spaces allotted to that variety."

¶*With all of which we are in accord.*

Kelway "Artistic" Herbaceous Borders

For Prices see page 49.

𝄏

" Plants diverse and strong,
That ev'ry day their blossoms change,
Ten thousand lovely hues !

With budding, fading, faded flowers,
They stand, the wonder of the bowers,
From morn to evening dews."

𝄏

Please give measurements and ask for plans under the following numbers, also say whether the borders are to be quite in the open or whether there is a backing of a wall or hedge or shrubs, and if so on which side.

𝄏

The Plans referred to are the registered copyright of Kelway & Son, Langport, the originators of their system, and may only be used by those to whom they have given permission, express or implied. It need hardly be mentioned that Kelway & Son expect those who take advantage of their system and plans to obtain the necessary plants from Langport.

𝄏

Whenever possible we recommend each sort being planted in *groups* of a kind as planned, as the general effect is then broader and more pleasing, but we can supply borders " boiled down " to any extent either as regards the varieties to be included or the number of plants of each kind to be used, and will give any information required as to borders of any kind.

𝄏

No. 1. The Kelway "Artistic" Permanent General Border

Arranged for Continuous Bloom and Colour effect.

An arrangement of a border containing a very wide range of plants that thrive in most gardens, including ("A" Selection) the newer and choicer of Kelway's and other introductions, planned in a graduated scheme of colour so as to delight the eye with harmonies and not to offend with unpleasant contrasts, and to be in bloom from the beginning to the end of the year.

The taller, stronger-growing kinds are arranged more or less at the back of the border, but rigid lines are not adhered to, and some of the plants of medium height and suitable habit are produced to the front edge, and some of the dwarf kinds of stout habit are allowed to run well back into the middle of the border.

We have made the selection from the most showy, hardy, and easily grown of the multitude of herbaceous perennial plants, including some of the most striking and satisfactory of new introductions, but not excluding prime old favourites on account of the time we have known them. No half-hardy or biennial kinds, such as Hollyhocks, Dahlias or Canterbury Bells, are included, but if desired they can easily be introduced.

The scheme, both as regards colour, continuity, and general suitability, is the outcome of KELWAY & SON's expert knowledge of this class of plant gained during the last half-century, and the result of its practical application for several recent years to the formation of their artistic herbaceous borders.

The plants are packed, labelled (and numbered in order for planting, if desired).

" A " SELECTION.

The cost of the selection, *if catalogue rates per plant or per dozen were adhered to,* would be very considerable, as a multitude of very choice improved varieties are included.

" B " SELECTION.

At the same time, while recommending "A" selection, by substituting less expensive varieties in the case of some of the Delphiniums, Pæonies, Gaillardias, Pyrethrums, etc., we supply a second selection (Selection "B").

Portions of this border, of any size or shape, are supplied at proportional prices.

𝄏

No. 2. Spring Flowering Borders

In flower from February to the end of May, arranged on the KELWAY " Artistic " plan of continuous bloom and colour effect.

No. 3. Summer Flowering Borders

In flower from May to August, arranged on the KELWAY "Artistic" plan of continuous bloom and colour effect.
For prices see No. 1.

*

No. 4. Autumn Flowering Borders

In flower from August to late in November, arranged on the KELWAY "Artistic" plan of continuous bloom and colour effect.
For prices see No. 1.

*

No. 5. Kelway Colour Borders

Or Borders OF ANY COLOUR OR SCHEME OF COLOUR required, either harmonies or contrasts, or borders, excluding any colour not liked ; pretty colour combinations left to us or according to the fancy of our clients. For instance, scarlets and crimsons and purple may be associated with blue and white ; and white, pink, light blue and lemon colour are a good combination, as also are purple, white and pink. As again, deep rose with blue and white, or deep yellow with purple and red.

*

No. 6. Kelway Pæony Borders

The flower of the century, the fashionable flower.

Garden Borders composed wholly or mainly of the Pæony family are now being formed, and are a very handsome addition to a garden of any size. Their actual flowering period extends through the months of May and June, but there is beauty in them from the latter days of March, when the crimson shafts, all ruddy with the warm promise of the coming summer, pierce the earth's crust, until the rich red browns of the passing leaves reflect the rays of the sun in autumn. Pæonies are so compact in root growth, and at the same time such sturdy strong-growing plants, as neither to injure suitable bulbs, etc., planted amongst them, nor to be harmed by the bulbs ; so that many lovely pictures can be formed with the background of the young Pæony growth in early spring, and of the matured foliage when summer is over. A bed with golden Daffodils mingled with the blood-coloured young Pæony shoots, and bordered by a delicate china-blue band of the "Glory of the Snow," is a sight which lingers in the memory long after the Pæonies have lapsed into their wealth of gorgeous summer blossoms, even until the flaming Gladioli tower over the masses of broad foliage in July and August and September, and cool their fiery hues against the colder, graceful beauty of Lilies and Galtonias.

The borders should consist, as far as the Pæonies are concerned, of KELWAY's June-flowering kinds.

The Bulbs, with the exception of the Lilies and Gladioli, will be planted in the autumn, the Pæonies any time between the end of August and March, and the Lilies and Gladioli in spring. Manure must be kept 9 inches underground where bulbs are.

*

No. 6a. May Flowering Pæonies

*

No. 7. Delphinium Borders

Magnificent improvement on the old perennial Larkspur.

If a KELWAY Pæony border is the most *brilliant*, the KELWAY Delphinium border is one of the most *beautiful* sights imaginable, chiefly because the colour blue predominates, a colour so full of joyful feeling and so precious in the garden. Those who have not seen KELWAY's Delphiniums well grown cannot imagine their wonderful loveliness.

*

No. 20. Kelway Michaelmas Daisy Borders

Delightful in the autumn with cool tints of grey, blue and lavender.

*

No. 24. Kelway Hardy Bulb Borders

In schemes of colour. Prices on application.

For other Borders see page 49.

KELWAY'S "ARTISTIC" BORDERS

No. 1 "A." Kelway "Artistic" permanent general Border. **£5 0s. 0d.** per 100 strong plants, or 10 square yards for **25/-**; 100 square yards **250/-**, arranged for continuous bloom and colour effect.

No. 1 "B" at **60/-** per 100; 10 square yards **15/-**; 100 square yards, **150/-**.

No. 2 "A." Spring Flowering Borders. In flower from February to the end of May, arranged on Kelway "Artistic" plan of continuous bloom and colour effect. Prices same as No. 1 "A."

No. 2 "B." Spring Flowering Borders. In flower from February to the end of May, arranged on Kelway "Artistic" plan of continuous bloom and colour effect. Prices same as No. 1 "B."

No. 3. Summer Flowering Borders, in flower from May to August, arranged on the Kelway "Artistic" plan of continuous bloom and colour effect. For prices see No. 1 "A" and No. 1 "B."

No. 4. Autumn Flowering Borders. In flower from August to late in November, arranged on the Kelway "Artistic" plan of continuous bloom and colour effect. For prices see No. 1 "A" and No. 1 "B."

No. 5. Kelway Blue Borders or Borders of any colour or scheme of colour required, either harmonies or contrasts; or borders excluding any colour not liked. Prices on application.

No. 6 "A." Kelway Pæony Borders, composed of Kelway's lovely large-flowered Pæonies. Per 100 Pæony plants (choice named kinds) from **£10**, or **20/-** per 10 square yards; with bulbs between, **40/-** per 10 square yards.

No. 6 "B." May Flowering Pæonies, per 100 pæony plants, **£5**, or **12/-** per 10 square yards; with bulbs between, **30/-** per 10 square yards.

No. 7. Kelway Delphinium Border. Those who have not seen Kelway's Delphiniums well grown cannot imagine their wonderful loveliness. Per 100 plants (choice kinds), from **£7 10s. 0d.** per 100; 10 square yards from **20/-**, **30/-**, **40/-**, upwards.

No. 8. Kelway Lupine Borders, composed of Kelway's Hybrid Lupines, white, all shades of soft yellows, lilacs, purples and blues. Prices on application.

No. 9. Kitchen Garden Flower Borders. Less expensive than other kinds. Prices on application.

No. 24. Kelway Hardy Bulb Borders. Prices on application.

No. 10. A North Border, for spring. Polyanthuses, &c. Prices on application.

No. 11. A South Border, for full sun. Prices on application.

No. 12. A Colour Border of Annual Flowers from seed. About 20 yards long × 3 yards, **25/-**, or a double border for **45/-**.

No. 13. A Border for Small Gardens in towns. Price on application.

No. 20. Kelway Michaelmas Daisy Border. Price on application.

¶ We supply, on the Kelway Plan, April Borders (No. 14), May Borders (No. 15), June Borders (No. 16), July Borders (No. 17), August Borders (No. 18), September Borders (No. 19), October Borders (No. 20), at prices of the General Kelway Border No. 1 "A" and No. 1 "B."

DOUBLE BORDERS

¶ A path between two borders with tracts of colour spreading to right and left gives a wonderfully fine effect. *All* the Kelway Borders can be so designed. Harmony is kept between the two borders, but one side is not a slavish or identical replica of the other.

¶ N.B. When Borders are less than 6ft. wide, we add 10% to the number of plants.

¶ When less than 3ft. wide, we add 20% plants and 10% to the charge.

¶ Borders for full *immediate* display are charged at an increased rate of 50%.

Kelway's Selections of Hardy Herbaceous Perennials for Special Purposes

Not Kelway's *Artistic* Selections.   These are Mixed Borders.

✤

" Call the vales and bid them hither cast
Their bells and flowerets of a thousand hues."
Milton.

✤

In a great number of cases it is convenient and satisfactory for our customers to mention **for what purpose** Hardy Perennial Plants are required, the space to be filled or the number of plants wanted, and to leave the detail of selection to ourselves. The names of the varieties are legion, and though of utmost importance to the initiated, are probably confusing to the general amateur public, and a matter of difficulty to select from.   Each kind is correctly labelled :—

1.—**BORDER SELECTION for BEAUTY IN THE GARDEN ;** plants tall, of medium height, and dwarf, and with a blooming period prolonged as far as possible throughout the year.

2.—**BORDER SELECTION of kinds specially suited for CUT FLOWERS for Vases, &c., as well as for garden effect ;** in other respects as No. 1. These have been called " Cut and Come Again Borders."

3.—**BORDER SELECTION for BEAUTY IN THE GARDEN IN SPRING, Tall, Medium and Dwarf.**

4.—**BORDER SELECTION for BEAUTY IN THE GARDEN IN SUMMER.   Tall, Medium and Dwarf.**

5.—**BORDER SELECTION for BEAUTY IN THE GARDEN IN AUTUMN.   Tall, Medium and Dwarf.**

N.B.—There are also plants for flowering in the WINTER in the open air, but not a large selection.

6.—**BORDER SELECTION for CUT FLOWERS IN SPRING.**

7.—**BORDER SELECTION for CUT FLOWERS IN SUMMER.**

8.—**BORDER SELECTION for CUT FLOWERS IN AUTUMN.**

9.—**BORDER SELECTION of DWARF KINDS.**

10.—**BORDER SELECTION of TALL KINDS.**

11.—**BORDER SELECTION of kinds of MEDIUM HEIGHT.**

12.—**BORDER SELECTION of kinds for HEAVY SOILS.**

13.—**BORDER SELECTION of kinds for LIGHT SOILS.**

14.—**BORDER SELECTION of kinds for SUNNY ASPECTS.**

15.—**BORDER SELECTION of kinds for COLDER SITUATIONS.**

18.—**SELECTION for SHRUBBERIES, kinds liking shade.**

19.—**WOODLAND SELECTION for rougher Shrubberies, Copses, &c., where the soil is never dug.**

20.—**WILD GARDEN SELECTION.**

The above selections are made up to any of the following values (roughly speaking, 3 to 4 plants for every 2s. charged ; but the inclusion of expensive varieties of Pæonies, Delphiniums, etc., by desire, will lessen the number of plants included:—

10/6, 15/-, 21/-, 25/-, 30/-, 36/-, 42/-, 50/-, 60/-, 75/-, or £5.

It is sufficient to order by number and price—e.g., " Selection No. 7 to the value of 60s.," with particulars, in some cases of, the space to be filled.   The dwarf border plants, and the rockery plants and the wild garden selection are less in price than the remainder.   In all cases better value is obtained by purchasing these collections, the selection of which is left to us, than where a customer chooses his own varieties by name.   It is at all times competent for a purchaser to request that we do not include certain varieties which he already possesses. ❧

KELWAY & SON, The Royal Horticulturists, LANGPORT, SOMERSET, ENGLAND

Recipients, for plants or strains of their own introduction or raising, and of their own growing, of 252 Grand Prizes and Gold and Silver Medals, at London, Paris, Chicago, St. Louis, Italy, &c., and more Certificates and Awards of Merit for improved varieties than any other firm.
Order now.   The Plants will be sent at the proper season.

KELWAY GARDEN SEATS *and* TRELLIS

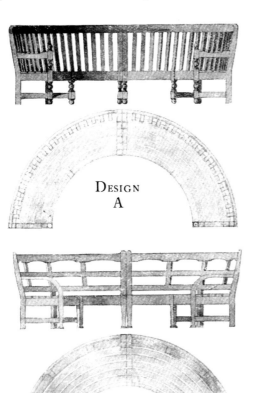

KELWAY QUADRANT SEATS

Design
A

Design
B

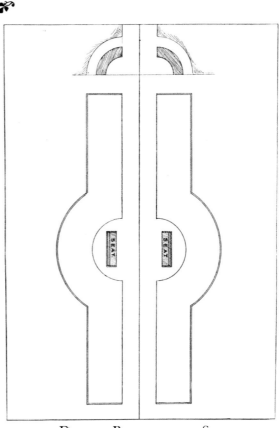

Double Border with Seats

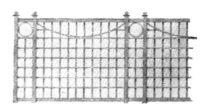

Kelway Trellis

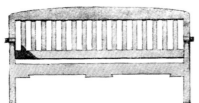

The Kelway Seat

The Pæony Seat

For prices see page 52.

KELWAY GARDEN SEAT
and TRELLIS

❧

PRICES

❧

SEATS.

	DEAL	OAK	TEAK
The Kelway Seat	£2 5s. 0d.	£3 10s. 0d.	£3 17s. 6d.
The Pæony Seat	£2 10s. 0d.	£3 17s. 6d.	£4 5s. 0d.

SEMI-CIRCULAR.

	DEAL	OAK	TEAK
Design A -	£7 10s. 0d.	£11 0s. 0d.	£12 5s. 0d.
Design B -	£8 0s. 0d.	£11 15s. 0d.	£13 5s. 0d.

KELWAY TRELLIS.

Per lineal yard as shown.

Deal Painted - - -	**8/6**
Deal Carbolineum - -	**7/-**
Oak Carbolineum - -	**10/6**
Oak from the saw plain - -	**10/-**
Oak, wrot fumed and oiled -	**13/6**

PERGOLA CHAIN.

3/9 per dozen yards.

LABELS.

THE KELWAY LABEL, in steel, for Herbaceous Plants, with the name of the plant in full, indelibly sunk in the metal. Unobtrusive, and lasting for ever. As we get these manufactured in large quantities, we offer them at the low rate of **30/-** per 100, or **4/-** per dozen.

SANDSTONE ROCKERY STONE.

In rough lumps at **4/-** per ton on rails at loading station.

BEST HARD YORKSHIRE STONE.

1½in. to 2in. self-faced broken paving in irregular-shaped pieces, **16/-** per ton.

A ton of the broken paving will cover about 9 superficial yards, say a space 9ft. 0in. by 9ft. 0in., 1½in. self-faced rectangular paving in random sizes, **3/6** per yard super. 1½in. self-faced rectangular paving, coursed one way, random the other, **4/-** per yard super.

We quote as above, on truck at loading station.

Albert Frost & Sons,
Printers, Rugby.